GEOLOGY OF THE JURASSIC COAST

THE ISLE OF PURBECK
WEYMOUTH TO STUDLAND

Paul Ensom and Malcolm Turnbull

A Coastal Publishing Book

Authors Paul Ensom & Malcolm Turnbull
Project Editor Professor Denys Brunsden, OBE
Editor Alison Moss
Design Jonathan Lewis
Publishing Manager Susan Sutterby

First Published in Great Britain 2011
by Coastal Publishing
The Studio, Puddletown Road
Wareham, Dorset BH20 6AE

www.coastalpublishing.co.uk
A Sillson Communications Ltd. Company

The Jurassic Coast Trust (Registered Charity No. 1101134) has been established to hold the proceeds of this publication, and other officially recognised products about the World Heritage Site. Funds will be used to support the conservation and education programmes for the Site.
www.jurassiccoasttrust.org

Enquiries concerning reproduction should be sent to Rights Department, Coastal Publishing, at the above address.

A Cataloguing in Publication (CIP) record for this book is available from the British Library.

Coastal Publishing and the authors have made every reasonable effort to locate, contact and acknowledge copyright owners and wish to be informed by any copyright owners who are not properly identified and acknowledged so that we may make any necessary corrections.

ISBN 978-1-907701-00-9

The Authors

Paul Ensom

Graduated from Leicester University in 1977 before joining the Dorset County Museum in Dorchester as Assistant Curator. In 1989 he became Keeper of Geology at the Yorkshire Museum and then in 1997 he moved to the Natural History Museum, London, as Collections Leader, Department of Palaeontology. He is currently an independent museum consultant and geologist and has recently published a book on Yorkshire geology. Paul is recognised as a skilled interpreter of geology and as an authority on the Purbeck Limestone Group's stratigraphy and palaeontology, including vertebrate tracks and other trace fossils, reptile eggshell and microvertebrates.

Malcolm Turnbull

Graduated from Durham University in 1968 before embarking on a career in commerce. In 1982 he and his family moved to Swanage and he joined Dorset County Council, first as a Ranger at Durlston Country Park, then as Coastal Policy Officer and finally as Manager of the Environment Policy Group. Malcolm was lead officer for Dorset County Council in the bid for World Heritage status for the Dorset and East Devon Coast, for which, in 2010, he and three other members of the core team were awarded the R.H. Worth Prize by the Geological Society of London. He is now retired, but continues to pursue his interest in coastal matters and is a trustee of the Jurassic Coast Trust.

The Jurassic Coast Trust

The Jurassic Coast Trust, established in 2002, is an independent registered charity governed by a board of trustees, which supports the delivery of science, conservation, arts, education and sustainable development programmes.

The Trust provides advice and influence and works with the Jurassic Coast World Heritage Team and other partners.

www.jurassiccoasttrust.org

CONTENTS

The 'Jurassic Coast' World Heritage Site

On 13 December 2001, the Dorset and East Devon coast, from Orcombe Point near Exmouth in Devon to Studland Bay in Dorset, was inscribed on the World Heritage List for its outstanding geology and geomorphology. The coast displays a unique, near continuous, sequence of rocks recording 265 million years of the Earth's history. The rocks, which cover the Triassic, Jurassic and Cretaceous periods of time, are superbly displayed in the dramatic, steadily eroding cliffs of the area. The strata tilt gently to the east so that, travelling from west to east, a walk along the coast will gradually take you up through time as you move from the oldest red sandstones of the Triassic through to the most recent white chalk cliffs of the Isle of Purbeck. It is 95 miles of outstandingly beautiful scenery that contains a globally important scientific record.

UNESCO only gives World Heritage status to sites that have an outstanding universal value to mankind. The Jurassic Coast ranks alongside the Grand Canyon and Yosemite National Park in the USA, the Great Barrier Reef in Australia, Dinosaur Provincial Park in Canada and Iguazu National Park in Argentina. In the words of His Royal Highness The Prince of Wales, the Jurassic Coast is 'a place of understanding and enjoyment, a scientific asset and an educational resource'.

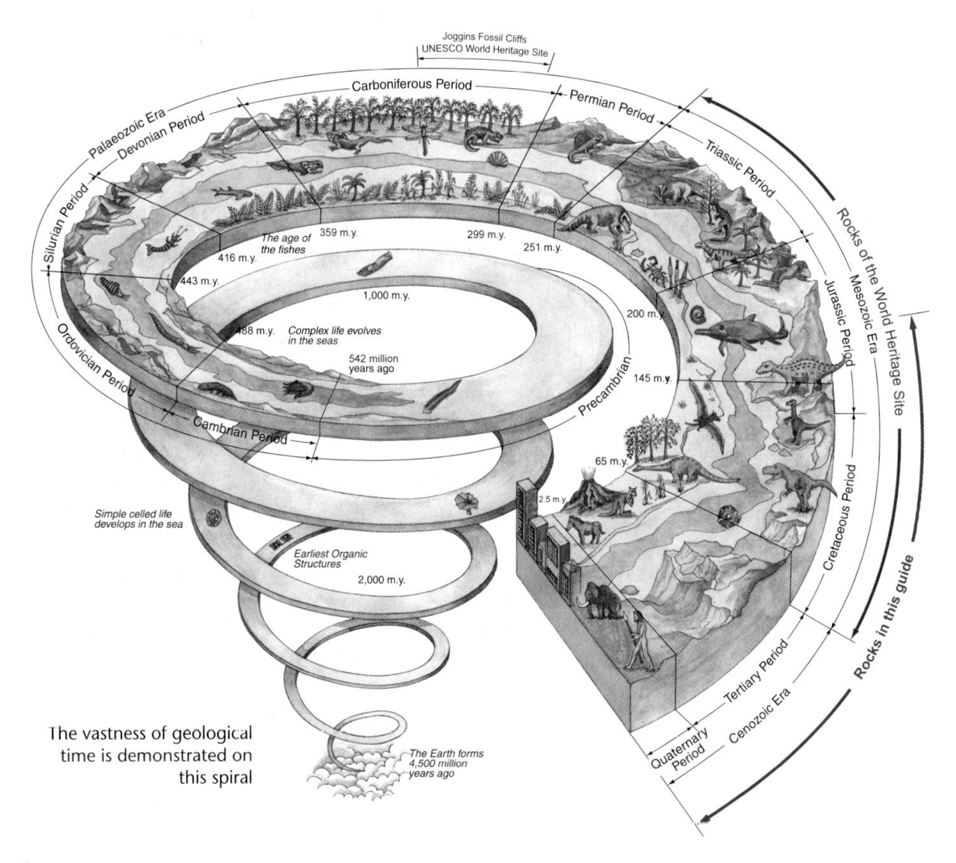

The vastness of geological time is demonstrated on this spiral

What will be the future of this ... coastline, so richly endowed as a training ground and museum of geology? Few tracts of equal size could raise so many claims, scientific, aesthetic and literary, for preservation ... If the English of the present generation allow this heritage of the community to be irreparably spoilt for private gain they will be held by posterity to have been unworthy to possess it.

W.J. Arkell, from *Geology of the Country around Weymouth, Swanage, Corfe and Lulworth* (1947)

As a World Heritage Site, the coast is managed 'on behalf of the whole of mankind' by the World Heritage Steering Group which is composed of representatives of organisations with an interest in the Dorset and East Devon coast. The designation brings no extra rules or regulations; indeed to qualify for World Heritage status, it is necessary to already have appropriate conservation measures in place. The Isle of Purbeck contains numerous areas of international designation – Special Area of Conservation and Special Protected Areas – and carries most of the UK's major designations – an Area of Outstanding Natural Beauty (AONB) and a Heritage Coast. In addition, there are a multitude of Sites of Special Scientific Interest (SSSIs) and Geological Conservation Review (GCR) sites. Offshore most of the waters are included in Natural England's proposed Marine Special Areas of Conservation.

Conservation designations may abound, but happily, with few exceptions, most of the coast is accessible to the public and is there to be enjoyed. The Purbeck coast offers a wealth of natural beauty and interest. The varied geology strongly influences the landforms and habitats, which in turn give rise to a remarkable variety of wildlife.

Introducing the Isle of Purbeck's Coast

A veritable crescendo of landforms and unique geology provides a fitting climax to the 95-mile (155km) west to east walk through time that is such a memorable feature of the World Heritage Site we know as the Jurassic Coast. The Purbeck coast is part of that once described by an eminent geologist as the 'cream of Dorset'. We could go even further by making a comparison with sparkling champagnes. After all, examples of these heady wines from the Aube district of that famed wine-growing region of France are created from grapes cultivated on rocks of equivalent age to the upper Kimmeridge Clay Formation. The formation's name derives from the small village nestling on this coast, a location irrevocably linked to the history and success of the UK oil industry. A very visual reminder of one aspect of this is the nodding donkey perched back from the cliff's edge, which has pumped oil from depth since the late 1950s.

Though this guide takes its name from an area of Dorset known as 'The Isle of Purbeck', a name with obscure origins for an island it is not, we include the coast from Furzy Cliff, just east of Weymouth, to Studland Bay, north of Swanage. Our approach is intentionally to provide an informed and mostly gentle introduction to the geology displayed on the Purbeck coast, with intelligible answers to those who wish to know why the cliffs look the way they do. Both landlubber and sailor will find this an invaluable aid to geological navigation along this classic coastline!

Special sections within the body of the guide provide insights into folds, faults and crumples, burning cliffs, collections and Victorian geologists. Geology is the foundation and framework

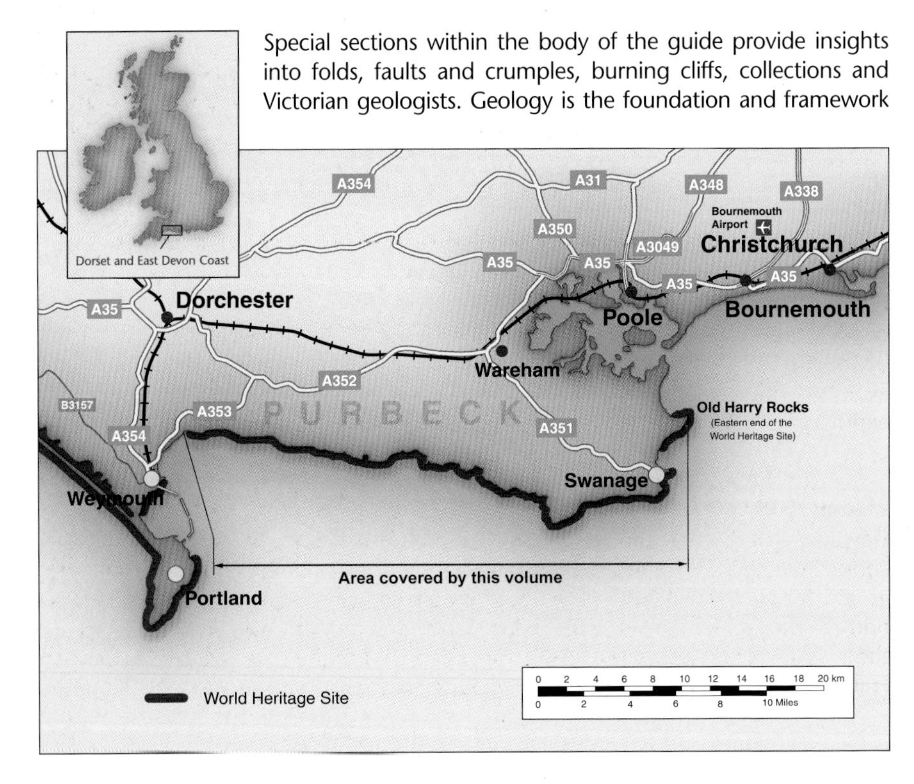

of the landscape and dictates the distribution of flora and fauna, how man has lived, and how the landscape will develop in the millennia to come. Appropriately, this guide touches on the plants and animals which have colonised and evolved on these Upper Jurassic and Cretaceous strata. The human story is narrated through sections on quarrying, cottages and castles, and on George Burt, who so nearly transformed the area to the south of Swanage, around Durlston, into an up-market housing estate! There are also sections on beaches, arches, stacks, reefs and races – and for those not put off by the latter, boat trips to be taken to view parts of this dramatic and beautiful coast.

The Geology of the Isle of Purbeck's Coast

William Jocelyn Arkell (1904–58)

'Dorset, to its many admirers, is the fairest county in England. The cream of Dorset is the coastline from Abbotsbury to Poole and its immediate hinterland.' So wrote that doyen of Jurassic geology, William Jocelyn Arkell, in the introduction to his classic memoir of the British Geological Survey, *The Geology of the Country around Weymouth, Swanage, Corfe and Lulworth*. The passage of over sixty years since the book's publication has provided new and exciting finds, data and insights, which have built on a key work that has inspired generations of geologists and informed all those interested in the often dramatic scenery of this coast. Our privilege is to be writing a guide which looks at a substantial part of that 'cream of Dorset', stretching from Furzy Cliff in the west (p. 42) to Studland Bay (p. 96) in the east. Arkell had recognised the uniqueness of the geology and geomorphology of that coastline, a uniqueness that provided the foundation for the successful bid for World Heritage status awarded in December 2001.

The 242-million-year story of the 'Jurassic Coast' was started in the *The Red Coast Revealed* (2008) and is here continued in 'chapters' spanning from around 165 Ma (million years ago) to the present day. Just as today, the layers of sediment represented include gravels, sands, silts, clays and limestones. They have been deposited in seas and on land over a deeply buried framework of older rocks riven by fractures called faults. These structures have exerted a powerful influence on the evolution of Dorset and are 'echoed' in the scenery we see today, the contemporary expression of a quite remarkable geological continuum.

Faults, Folds and Crumples

Deep below Dorset, an ancient buried landscape carries the scars of an episode of continental collision called the Variscan Orogeny, which may have begun as early as 380 Ma and ended 285 Ma. During this time, what is now Britain lay just to the north of the Equator. A land mass called Gondwana was moving northward, pushing the smaller continents called Iberia (Spain and Portugal) and Armorica (northern France) into Laurussia, of which Britain was a part.

This collision produced a variety of east to west trending structures, including folds and faults associated with great east to west mountain chains, which were thrown up across southern Britain and parts of Europe. There were volcanic eruptions, and the formation of the granites, which include Dartmoor in Devon and Bodmin and Carnmellis in Cornwall. All this may seem remote from the Isle of Purbeck and south Dorset, yet along a line from the Isle of Wight, through Poole Harbour to Abbotsbury, ancient structures which formed all those millions of years ago have continued to influence our landscapes. Over this landscape, with its cover of Permian sediments, rocks of the Triassic, Jurassic, Cretaceous (all Mesozoic), Paleogene and Neogene (both Cenozoic) periods have been deposited to create the Jurassic Coast.

As plate tectonics has applied stresses and strains to the fabric of southern Dorset, strata have been folded and faults reactivated or formed anew. In addition, ancient deposits of salt beneath parts of southern Dorset have been squeezed, flowing like a viscous fluid. As a result of these processes, layers of sediment have accumulated in some places but not others, and other rocks have been uplifted and eroded.

The coast provides the visitor to Dorset with a series of windows, some more accessible than others, through which to view several dramatic episodes in our past – folds, crumples, faults and unconformities, the results of these huge forces.

A traverse of the coast from west to east reveals a wide variety of rock types in very different attitudes of repose and relationship to the sea. These different characteristics have provided the geological framework for the evolution of the coast (pp. 12 and 62).

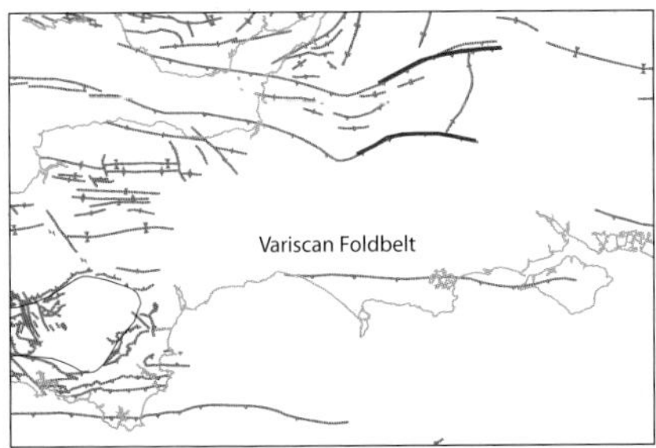

East–west structures visible in central and western Devon and parts of Somerset are buried beneath more recent strata to the east. One deeply buried east–west Variscan (380–285 Ma) structure is shown running from Abbotsbury, beneath the Isle of Purbeck, to the Isle of Wight. This underlies the Abbotsbury–Ridgeway Fault (ARF) and Purbeck–Wight Disturbance (PWD) labelled ARF and PWD in the next image.

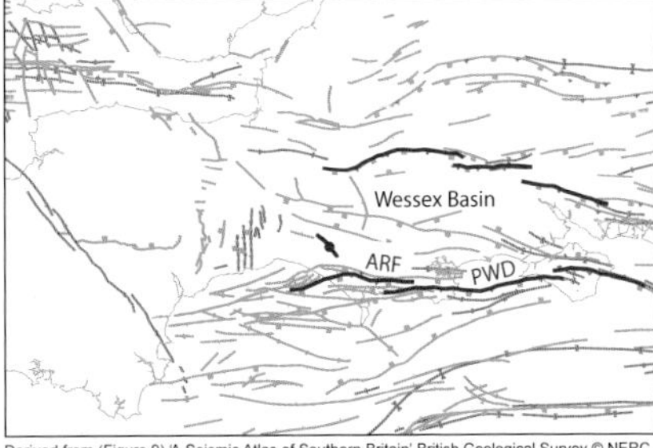

More recent east–west structures (285 Ma to present), represented by green, orange and purple lines and rarely preserved across Devon, where the younger rocks were either not deposited or have been subsequently stripped away, are visible where younger rocks (Triassic–Cretaceous) are preserved over eastern-most Devon, much of Somerset, and from Dorset into Hampshire. ARF and PWD.

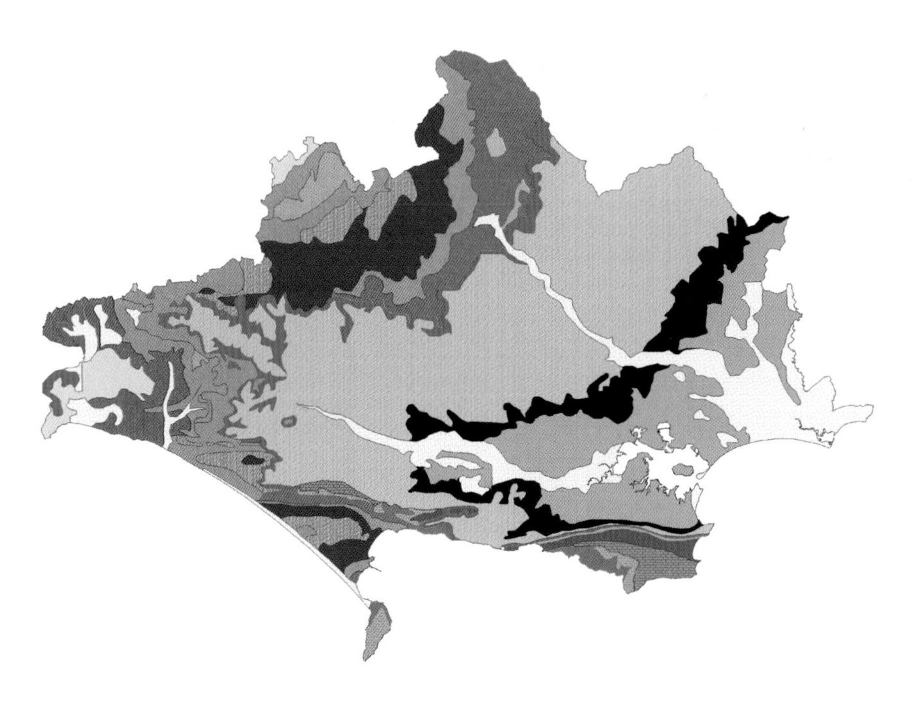

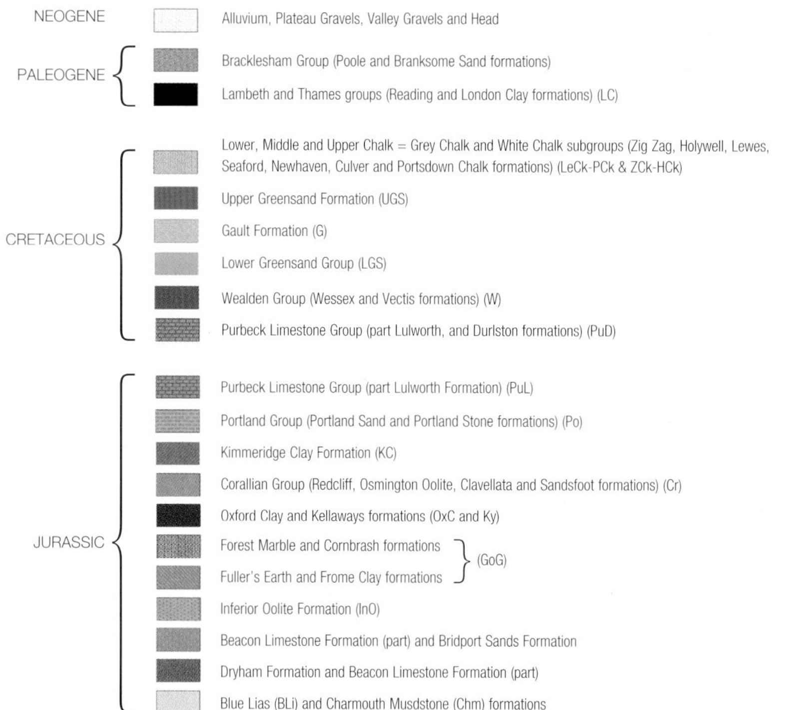
NEOGENE
Alluvium, Plateau Gravels, Valley Gravels and Head
PALEOGENE
Bracklesham Group (Poole and Branksome Sand formations)
Lambeth and Thames groups (Reading and London Clay formations) (LC)
CRETACEOUS
Lower, Middle and Upper Chalk = Grey Chalk and White Chalk subgroups (Zig Zag, Holywell, Lewes, Seaford, Newhaven, Culver and Portsdown Chalk formations) (LeCk-PCk & ZCk-HCk)
Upper Greensand Formation (UGS)
Gault Formation (G)
Lower Greensand Group (LGS)
Wealden Group (Wessex and Vectis formations) (W)
Purbeck Limestone Group (part Lulworth, and Durlston formations) (PuD)
JURASSIC
Purbeck Limestone Group (part Lulworth Formation) (PuL)
Portland Group (Portland Sand and Portland Stone formations) (Po)
Kimmeridge Clay Formation (KC)
Corallian Group (Redcliff, Osmington Oolite, Clavellata and Sandsfoot formations) (Cr)
Oxford Clay and Kellaways formations (OxC and Ky)
Forest Marble and Cornbrash formations
Fuller's Earth and Frome Clay formations
(GoG)
Inferior Oolite Formation (InO)
Beacon Limestone Formation (part) and Bridport Sands Formation
Dryham Formation and Beacon Limestone Formation (part)
Blue Lias (BLi) and Charmouth Musdstone (Chm) formations

Three sections showing the complex structures, as interpreted by the British Geological Survey, which have conspired to produce the unique geology of the Isle of Purbeck. For key to strata codes see Key to map p.11.

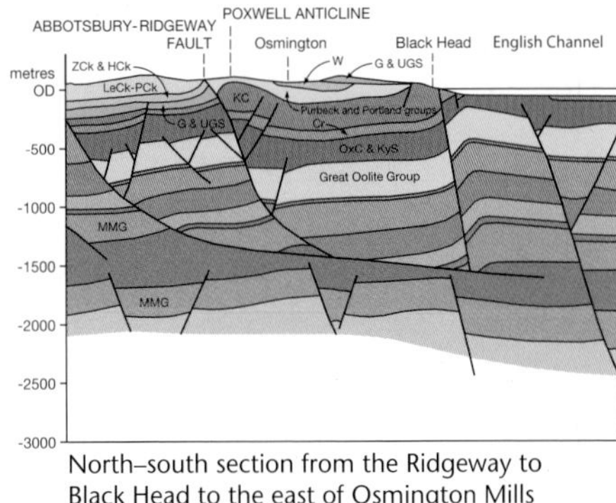

North–south section from the Ridgeway to Black Head to the east of Osmington Mills

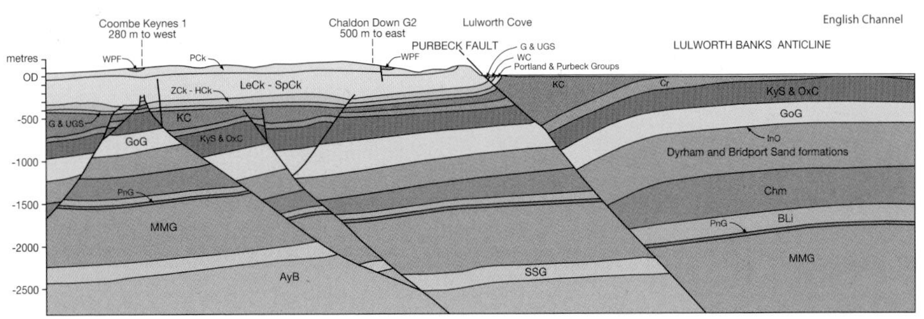

North–south section from near Coombe Keynes through Lulworth Cove

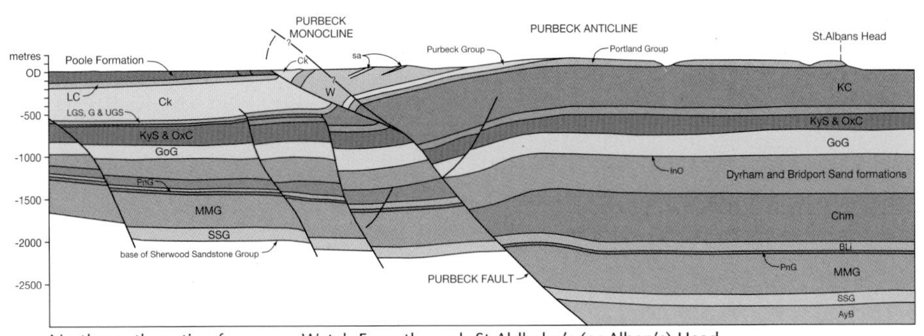

North–south section from near Wytch Farm through St Aldhelm's (or Alban's) Head

A famous and obvious example of the impact of the Alpine Orogeny on a series of limestones and clays is the formation of the great crumple so dramatically seen at Stair Hole (pp. 40-41), near Lulworth Cove. This formed when strata overlying the reactivated and reversed Purbeck Fault (previously strata were being stretched and had slipped down to the south, but were now compressed and pushed back up in the opposite direction) were tilted to a high angle, and the relatively soft clays were unable to support the weight of the interleaved beds of limestone. The strata collapsed downwards, forming the famous crumple.

The coastline described in this guide lies astride the hinge between what for much of this time has been a 'block' to the north and a 'basin' to the south, features inherited from the earlier upheavals (pp. 9–10). From time to time, they have been tilted to the east. The red rocks exposed on the East Devon coast, which pass up into the Lower Jurassic marine muds, silts, sands and limestones exposed along the West Dorset coast, dip gradually eastwards; at Kimmeridge Bay the brilliant yellow Bridport Sands exposed in the cliffs between West Bay and Burton Bradstock extend down 1,000m beneath your feet.

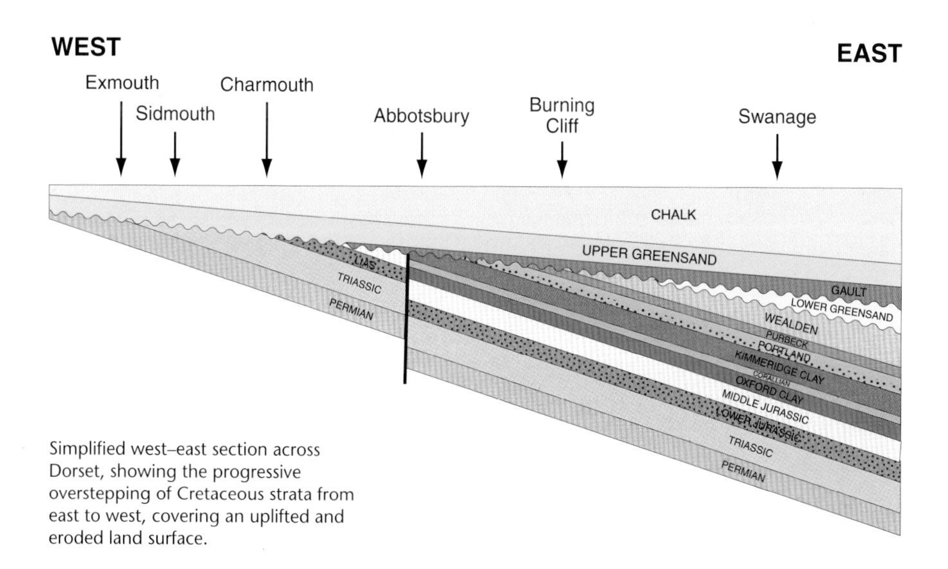

Simplified west–east section across Dorset, showing the progressive overstepping of Cretaceous strata from east to west, covering an uplifted and eroded land surface.

Naming and Dating the Rocks

Geologists studying the rocks that make up the Earth have devised a variety of methods of linking rocks in different places. William Smith (1769–1839), who is known as the Father of British geology, recognised the significance of the different groups of fossils that different rocks contained. His remarkable perception allowed him to predict what rocks should be met with during mining, canal building and other engineering projects. This predictive approach led to the development of biostratigraphy, relying on the fossilised remains of different animals and plants as they evolved through time. Their presence in different layers of rock allowed him to develop an organised sequence of fossil-bearing rocks in the United Kingdom, and enabled him to produce the first geological map of much of the UK.

Some organisms were recognised as evolving quite rapidly and were fortuitously widespread in their occurrence. Find one in sandstone at x, in limestone at b, and shale at p, and you know you have rocks of almost exactly the same age. Another way of linking rocks is by using the record of the Earth's magnetic field preserved in the rocks. Because the magnetic field periodically undergoes reversal, there is an opportunity to use this to link sequences of rock in widely separated places. By taking very accurately orientated samples back to the laboratory, the 'fossilised' magnetic field can be detected and read.

The composition of rocks, i.e. their lithology, allows geologists to define nameable units that should be easy to recognise and map (p. 11). The smallest unit is a bed, one or more of which form a member. A number of members comprise a formation, and normally two or more formations make a group. Beds may be named on the basis of some distinctive characteristic, e.g. 'The Crocodile Bed', because it contains crocodile remains. Members may be similarly named, or like formations and groups, take their names from where the strata are especially well exposed, e.g. Redcliff Formation, and Purbeck Limestone Group (p. 26).

Embracing these different approaches to the correlation of rocks, there is chronostratigraphy. Here we confront our desire to date what we see and find. The radiometric dating of rocks has advanced very quickly since Ernest Rutherford recognised the significance of the decay of radioactive isotopes in the early 1900s. The rate of decay varies considerably, and geophysical laboratories are able to measure this, dating rocks as far back as when the Earth was formed. These processes are still being refined and made more accurate. Dated rocks containing fossils or evidence of a widely recognised event such as a glaciation or volcanic eruption allows us to impose progressively more or less constrained timescales on the rocks of the world. Each of the stratigraphic sections that follow this introduction provide dates for the rocks being described.

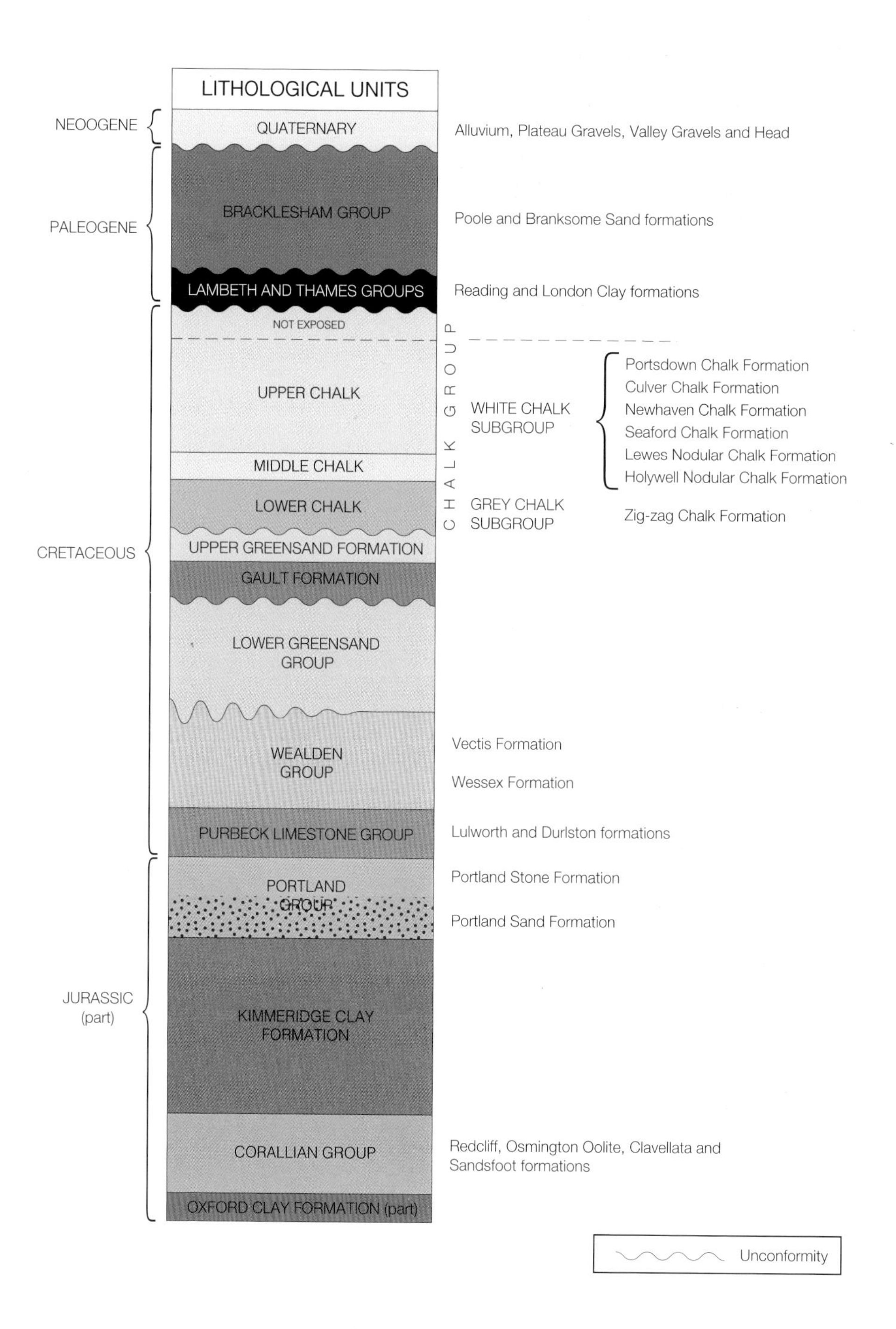
LITHOLOGICAL UNITS
NEOOGENE
QUATERNARY
Alluvium, Plateau Gravels, Valley Gravels and Head
PALEOGENE
BRACKLESHAM GROUP
Poole and Branksome Sand formations
LAMBETH AND THAMES GROUPS
Reading and London Clay formations
NOT EXPOSED
CHALK GROUP
UPPER CHALK
WHITE CHALK SUBGROUP
Portsdown Chalk Formation
Culver Chalk Formation
Newhaven Chalk Formation
Seaford Chalk Formation
Lewes Nodular Chalk Formation
Holywell Nodular Chalk Formation
MIDDLE CHALK
LOWER CHALK
GREY CHALK SUBGROUP
Zig-zag Chalk Formation
CRETACEOUS
UPPER GREENSAND FORMATION
GAULT FORMATION
LOWER GREENSAND GROUP
WEALDEN GROUP
Vectis Formation
Wessex Formation
PURBECK LIMESTONE GROUP
Lulworth and Durlston formations
PORTLAND GROUP
Portland Stone Formation
Portland Sand Formation
JURASSIC (part)
KIMMERIDGE CLAY FORMATION
CORALLIAN GROUP
Redcliff, Osmington Oolite, Clavellata and Sandsfoot formations
OXFORD CLAY FORMATION (part)
Unconformity

Introducing the Rocks of the Purbeck Coast

Before embarking on our west to east traverse of the 'Purbeck' coast, there follow short sections to set the scene, an introduction to the 'strata dramatis', the characters which provide the almost unbelievable 165-million-year pageant of this coast. The oldest rocks are predominantly exposed in the west and the youngest in the east. They represent marine, marginal marine and terrestrial environments.

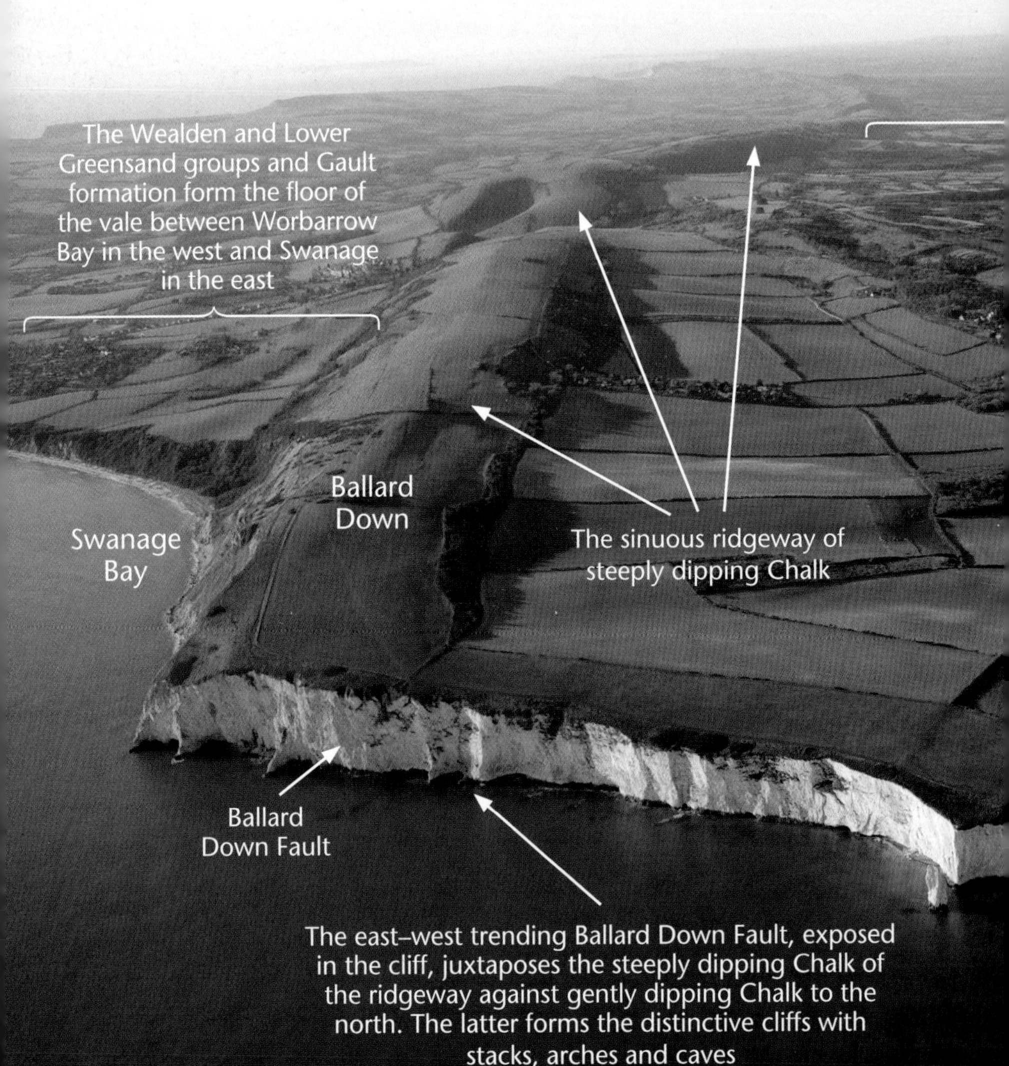

An aerial view of the Isle of Purbeck demonstrates the profound effects of the underlying geology on the physical relief, vegetation and land use

There are ammonite-rich muds and coccolith oozes, shallow-water shelly limestones with a wide variety of molluscs, sediments which today one has to travel to the Gulf States and North Africa to find, mud-cracked surfaces with the tracks of dinosaurs, and coarse grits and sands deposited by rivers which carried great rafts of vegetation in times of flood.

Paleogene and Neogene sands and gravels of the Dorset heaths north of the ridgeway

Poole Harbour

Studland Bay

The Foreland or Handfast Point with Old Harry and his latest wife!

First to appear are the mostly muddy Oxford Clay Formation and overlying Corallian Group with its coral reefs and ancient oil reservoir preserved in the cliffs at Osmington (pp. 42-43). There follows the great thickness of brooding Kimmeridge Clay Formation, with its dark secrets of oxygen-starved environments, burning cliffs and the rich vertebrate fauna found within its black shales; during this period, the great marine reptiles thrived. The Portland Group, source of the famed Portland Stone exploited to such brilliant effect by Sir Christopher Wren, and containing some of the largest coiled ammonites to be seen in the UK, and the overlying layered Purbeck Limestone Group's remarkable tale of salt flats and sabkahs fringed by coastal forests, and of the fishes, tiny amphibians, lizards, turtles, crocodiles and dinosaurs. In parallel to all this drama, the story of the evolution of mammals is another part of this coast's amazing narrative (p. 26). Mammals, still only in the earlier stages of their evolutionary path, were recovered from an 1852 excavation near Swanage, reported by Charles Kingsley, a famous author of the day, in the *Illustrated London News* (p. 89): the tiny fossils discovered then still underpin research around the world today. The Wealden Group's vibrantly coloured clays and grits, plant-rich beds and rare dinosaur bones mark the Mesozoic zenith of the terrestrial environment on this coast, soon to be inundated by an ever deepening and more extensive sea which saw the Lower Greensand Group, Gault and Upper Greensand formations, and Chalk Group deposited. The Chalk sea retreated and there was uplift, further folding and erosion. A fine balance between land and sea led to the deposition of the sediments of the Lambeth and Poole formations and the overlying sands and gravels which make up the heaths to the north of the Chalk ridgeway, the hog's back of Chalk that runs from Ballard Point in the east to West Lulworth, and then in a more subdued but still elevated form west to White Nothe and on to Abbotsbury before continuing northwards.

Geomorphological processes have been shaping the surface of the Earth throughout geological time, and Dorset's landscape is the product of their most recent activity. Acting on the wide variety of rock types and structures, they have created the varied landscapes inland, and the wealth of coastal landforms including bays, coves, natural arches and stacks. Rockslides and landslides provide dynamic and dramatic evidence of this continuum.

Muddy Waters: The Oxford Clay Formation, 164.7–159.5 Ma

The cliffs to the north and east of Weymouth (p. 42), as far as Shortlake, south of Osmington (p. 42), are mostly or partially composed of clay and silty clay belonging to the Upper Oxford Clay Formation. They are relatively soft and easily eroded, which means that along much of the coast good exposures are hard to find.

Deposited in a marine environment, these mudrocks are frequently very fossiliferous, yielding everything from the tiniest of microfossils, through large oyster shells and other bivalves, gastropods, belemnites and ammonites, to the remains of large marine reptiles such as plesiosaurs and ichthyosaurs. Some of these fossils are preserved in nodules of hardened clay, a particularly well-known occurrence at Furzy Cliff being the Red Nodule Beds, so called on account of their orangey-red colour.

Their presence has been put down to a slowing in the rate at which the sediment accumulated.

Recent research using the shells of some of the invertebrate fossils has shown that, while these deposits were being laid down, sea temperatures ranged from an average of 11.8°C on the sea floor to 15°C in the surface waters – a temperature which compares with the mean temperature of the northern Spanish coast today.

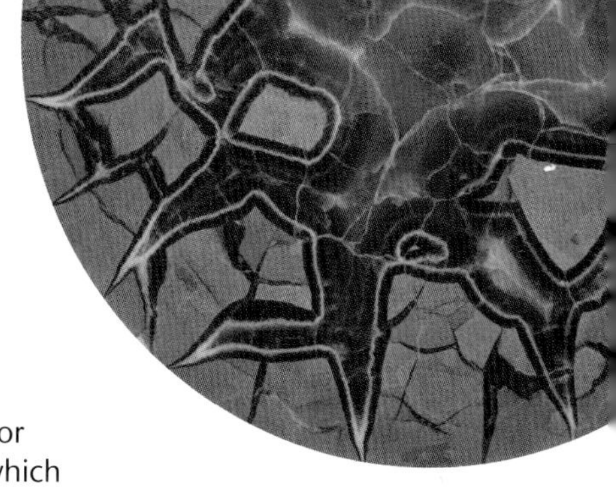

A cut and polished septarian nodule from the Oxford Clay.

Some beds have had a significant economic importance both locally and nationally. They have been extensively quarried for the manufacture of bricks, using their high hydrocarbon content to assist with the firing process. Brick pits existed at Chickerell near Weymouth, and especially in the great brickfields of Bedfordshire, north of London. This same organic-rich clay has contributed as a source rock to some of the oil fields across the UK. While never competing with the clays for brick production, a charming use was found for the often substantial septarian nodules which occur in these strata. They were sometimes sliced and used for tabletops.

Shallow Seas: The Corallian Group, 159.5–154.7 Ma

Corals are sometimes abundant in rocks of this age, hence Corallian. In south Dorset corals are rare but did briefly flourish during a shallow, clear-water prelude to the muddy and deeper-water Kimmeridge Clay Formation.

Below these coral-bearing beds, between Bowleaze Cove (p. 42) and Ringstead Bay (p. 43), is a varied sequence of clays, silts and sands, and different types of limestone of mostly marine origin. They formed in a range of water depths. Sometimes there is evidence of a freshwater influence: the Bencliff Grit Member is thought to be a tidally influenced deposit, probably at the mouth of an estuary. The nature of the sediments and their fossil content provides clues: mud with marine fossils generally represents deeper off shore water, and coarser silts, sands and limestones, sometimes rich in thick-shelled marine molluscs or their remains, are indicative of shallow water conditions.

During this period sea levels fluctuated and different researchers studying these strata have variously recognised both four and six variations: disagreements over such events are not unusual between geologists!

In the 1930s, the Bencliff Grit caught the eye of geologists assessing the likelihood of finding oil beneath Dorset. Exposed in the cliff near Bran Point (p. 43) they found an ancient long-breached oil reservoir, and there is reputed to be a small oil-seep on the foreshore. On hot sunny days you can smell the oil, and there is a slightly tarry feel to some layers, all that remains of the 'black gold' once contained there. The Bencliff Grit is also the source of the great spherical nodules known as doggers that litter parts of the shore. They are present where the usually soft silty sand has been turned to stone (lithified). A possible explanation for this process might be the presence of vertical burrows through the sediment, later acting as a conduit for fluids carrying a natural cement. Their irregular shape could be explained by variations in the permeability and porosity of the sediment.

Countless millions of tiny spheres of calcium carbonate called ooliths, like these from the coast of Abu Dhabi, are present in the Osmington Oolite Member at Bran Point between Osmington Mills and Ringstead Bay.

Another especially memorable rock type are the oolitic limestones within the Osmington Oolite Formation, white to cream-coloured and composed of billions of tiny spheres or ooliths of

Very large spherical nodules, also known as doggers, emerge from the unconsolidated sandy silts of the Bencliff Grit Member in the cliffs east of Osmington Mills.

calcium carbonate, which en masse resemble coarse fish roe; *òion* is Greek for 'egg'. Today's coasts of the Gulf States and Bahamas have deposits like this, forming in higher temperatures than we boast in the UK today.

Organic Rich Shales: The Kimmeridge Clay Formation, 154.7–147.6 Ma

The superb exposures and immense thickness of this formation visible in brooding cliffs around Kimmeridge (p. 68) led to the adoption of the name 'Kimmeridge Clay' by William Smith in 1816 to describe these hugely important beds. The formation attains a thickness of around 460m on the Dorset coast, and is among the thickest sequences of mudrocks in the UK. They characterise increasingly significant parts of the cliff sections from just east of Shortlake (p. 42) eastwards to Kimmeridge Bay and on to Chapman's Pool (p. 69). On the shore between Emmetts Hill and St Aldhelm's (or Alban's) Head, there are the easternmost small exposures of the Kimmeridge Clay Formation (p. 77).

What were conditions like when these strata were deposited? We know they changed significantly following the shallow and clear waters that supported the growth of corals at the end of the Corallian. Very different views on the depth of the Kimmeridge sea have been expressed, ranging from less than 10m to several hundred metres. Detailed study of the sediments at both macro and microscopic scales, and of the fossils and their preservation, has led to a consensus that the Kimmeridge sea had a maximum depth of 100m.

Among the predominantly grey mudrocks seen at Kimmeridge Bay, the yellow stone bands in the cliffs and forming the ledges stand out. These stone bands are dolomites. Their chemistry indicates that they formed after the sediments had been buried and in the presence of methane. The Kimmeridge Clay Formation along the Dorset coast is likely to have been buried to a depth of 2km.

The variations in the sediment accumulating on the sea floor are superbly preserved and highly visible to the observer as distinctive banding present in many of the cliff sections. Such banding has a story to tell which has been the focus of scientific endeavour and debate over many decades. The repetitive nature of the different layers is probably explained by variations in global climate caused by the Earth's varying orbit of the sun, and the wobble about our axis of rotation. They are a kind of astronomical clock. The white bands represent the enormous blooms of the marine algae called coccoliths. The preservation of these bands was once thought to be a consequence of water depth, where the greatest water depths protected these delicate structures and led to their preservation. The most likely reason proposed is the development of a pronounced temperature stratification of the water, known as a thermocline, a protecting watery blanket: events such as winter storms and rarer tsunami rarely disrupted this. The lack of circulation in this stratified water column progressively led to de-oxygenation of the deeper waters. Without oxygen, nothing lived and organic-rich sediments accumulated on a stagnant sea floor. Strata such as these are described as a black shale formation. The relative abundance of organic rich shales at different locations is regarded as a good indicator of water depth – the more there are, the deeper the water had been. Fine sediments from the upper

The north–western end of Brandy Bay, immediately east of Gad Cliff. This view shows the Upper and part of the Middle Kimmeridge Clay Formation, which has been cut by three small faults. These are shown as dashed lines with an arrow on the down-thrown side. The characteristic stone bands demonstrate the movement along the faults. Note that the two left-hand faults have juxtaposed pervious against impervious strata, leading to the formation of springs and consequently landslipping. WSB = White Stone Band; B = Blackstone, which is an oil shale.

warmer and oxygenated waters rained down to evenly cover the inhospitable sea floor. If the two water masses mixed, oxygen was at least briefly introduced to the deeper water and life would flourish for a short space of time, until the thermocline became re-established.

The organic-rich shales have great economic importance as oil-source rocks in the North Sea. Locally they have been used as a variety of 'coal' for both domestic and industrial purposes (p. 76), and have fuelled burning cliffs along this coastline. They were once exported to be distilled to produce fuel and other chemicals. The oil shales were interbedded with mudstones and coccolith limestones deposited over a period of around 7 million years.

The Kimmeridge Clay has yielded a fossil fauna which is best described as fabulous, providing vivid 'snapshots' of the life and times of an outwardly uninspiring-looking deposit (see pp. 74-75 and 90).

The Burning Cliffs

Burning cliffs are potentially spectacular and Dorset is remarkable for having witnessed several examples, which have been documented. The earliest was in 1751 at Charmouth (NGR SY 365 930), and the most recent in 1972 at Kimmeridge (p. 68). There was a near miss at Charmouth in 1987 when there was sufficient heat to make the cliff steam, but not ignite. Evidence of another is found at Small Mouth (NGR SY 668 762) near Weymouth. Two examples are recorded from the coast described in this guide, the most westerly at Ringstead below Holworth House, and one to the east of Kimmeridge, mentioned above. Inevitably they attracted considerable interest with their smoking fumaroles – shades of volcanism!

The Holworth cliff (p. 43) was observed burning from 1826 until 1829 and the one at Clavell's Hard, a little to the east of Kimmeridge Bay, from 1972 until 1974.

Cliff falls may be the trigger. Air reaching hitherto buried sediments reacts with unstable iron pyrite. The decay of pyrite, and possibly bacterial activity, create heat and the ignition of organic-rich shale may result. The example at Clavell's Hard was especially well studied where the hydrocarbon-rich Blackstone fuelled this burning cliff. Temperatures below the surface reached over 500°C, achieving red heat. The shale was baked and reddened to look like roof tiles, and sulphur dioxide and water vapour were present in the gases given off. Minerals found around the fumaroles included

An anonymous engraving of the 1826–29 fire.

A fumarole at the site of the burning cliff (1972–74), Clavell's Hard, east of Kimmeridge. Above is the Rope Lake Head stone band.

sulphur, ammonium chloride, gypsum, bassanite and anhydrite. Black tarry oil was present as a condensate.

Limestones for Buildings: The Portland Group, 147.6–144.8 Ma

The Portland Group is divided into two, the lower Portland Sand Formation and overlying Portland Stone Formation. Their names come from the Isle of Portland, visible on a clear day to the south-west from the Purbeck coast. They have a combined thickness, which ranges from 40m at Ringstead (p. 43) to 110m between Gad Cliff (p. 68) and Chapman's Pool (p. 69), a mere 20km away. This extraordinary variation has been linked to Earth movements taking place during their deposition. These were triggered by either movement along the older and deeply buried east–west faults previously referred to or the upward movement of thick deposits of Triassic salt, or possibly a combination of both. The Portland Sand carries on the 'coarser-grained theme' seen at the top of the Kimmeridge Clay. Muddy silts and fine sands accumulated. These have been dolomitised, a process that is believed to result from magnesium-rich brines flowing from the enclosed basin's arid fringes into deeper water. Here they have altered the calcium carbonate in the sediments into calcium magnesium carbonate, forming dolomites. The Portland Sand becomes increasingly fossiliferous higher in the deposit. Fossils are usually preserved as casts and moulds – the shell is not preserved. The different beds have distinctive names based on localities where they are well exposed or on their physical characteristics. Examples are the Emmit Hill Marls and Black Sandstones.

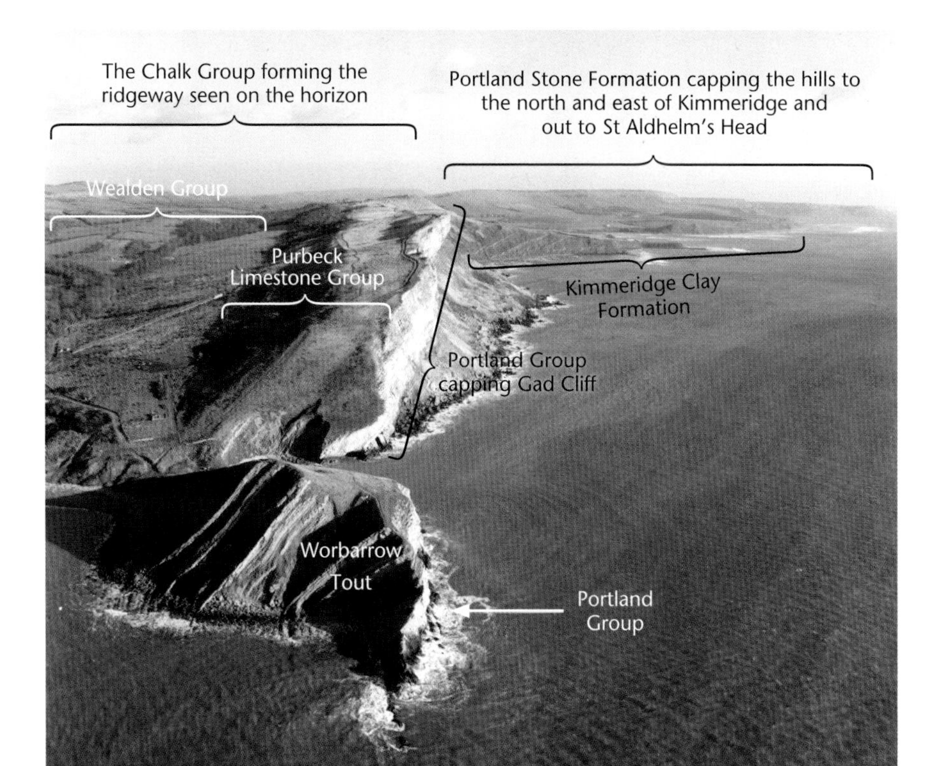

The Portland Group is comprised of the Portland Sand and overlying Portland Stone formations. The latter forms the solid bulwark against the sea at Worbarrow Tout in the foreground. The Portland Stone then rises up, forming the jagged crest of Gad Cliff, with Portland Sand and Kimmeridge Clay formations below. Followed east, it turns inland to form the escarpment which encompasses the tiny village of Kimmeridge. The formation then tops the hills to the east, before, in the distance, it is seen capping the imposing St Aldhelm's Head, the distant headland in this photograph.

The overlying Portland Stone Formation, while showing some variation along the coast, is divided primarily into a lower series of limestones, which are rich in bands of chert, and an upper series, which on the Isle of Purbeck is known slightly confusingly as the Portland Freestone – 'Purbeck Portland'! As on Portland, the limestones have been quarried for hundreds of years: quarries are still active in these strata on the Isle of Purbeck. Many of the beds boast charming names such as Prickle Bed or Puffin Ledge, Listy Bed, Pond Freestone and Shrimp Bed (p. 84). The limestones are off-white to cream and even greyish. Substantially they consist of the detritus of life, faecal pellets and fragments of shell; they are sometimes oolitic. They are at times richly fossiliferous. Trace fossils left by crustaceans form extensive horizontal, branching burrow systems, and there are many different molluscs, among which the gigantic ammonites, so characteristic of these strata, are numbered. The Portland Stone Formation is responsible for some of the most dramatic coastal scenery covered in this guide.

Lagoons and Mudflats: The Purbeck Limestone Group, 144.8–136.8 Ma

Among the diverse strata exposed along the Jurassic Coast, the sequence composed predominantly of limestone, clay and shale dating from around 140 Ma, and named after the Isle of Purbeck, where exposures abound, is the one that would so easily provide the characters to populate the pages of a book titled 'Cretaceous Park'. From at least the 1850s, a remarkably rich and often exquisitely preserved range of plants and invertebrate and vertebrate animals has been recovered which permits scientists and artists to reconstruct the environment with the flora and fauna.

An artist's idealised reconstructions of lake/lagoon margin and lagoonal environments which existed over what is now the Isle of Purbeck during the deposition of the Purbeck Limestone Group. The reconstructions have been based on the abundant fossilised remains of plants, invertebrates and vertebrates including mammals.

The rocks of the Purbeck Limestone Group were deposited across a hinge between terrestrial and aquatic environments, with the Purbeck landscape south of what is now the Chalk ridgeway slowly sinking, sometimes rather more rapidly when movements along local faults took place. The greatest thickness (*c.*119m) of the Purbeck sediments along this coast is recorded in Durlston Bay (p. 77). Subsidence led to the burial and preservation of organisms which had died, and of the tracks of dinosaurs (pp. 28–9) across the unconsolidated sediments both in and around the lakes and lagoons. A snapshot in the time of 'Cretaceous Park' was guaranteed and ongoing research continues to add colour to our picture of pre historic life across Dorset.

Today a useful comparison might be made with Poole Harbour, where sediments are accumulating in the fringing low-lying salt marshes on the north side of the fold axis of the Purbeck Monocline, which follows the line of the Chalk ridgeway; birds, the descendants of the dinosaurs, leave their tracks along the shores of Poole Harbour.

Dinosaur tracks are at times abundant in the Purbeck Limestone Group. Here is an artist's reconstruction of an environment where dinosaurs wander across unconsolidated sediment, leaving behind tracks.

Tracks of Dinosaurs

Dinosaur tracks are a variety of trace fossil. They were first recognised in the Purbeck strata of Dorset in Victorian times, though accurate records of where they had originated were not kept. Coastal and inland quarries and quarrs are likely to have been their source.

In the second half of the twentieth century, a series of remarkable discoveries led to an increasing appreciation of what these trace fossils could tell us about the environments and ways in which the dinosaurs lived. Surprisingly, the way in which a bipedal (two-legged) dinosaur walked was still far from understood until the 1960s. A discovery in a quarry on the outskirts of Swanage revealed a pair of tracks which ran parallel for some distance and then suddenly diverged. One dinosaur stomping along with its feet placed wide apart had suddenly become two dinosaurs placing one foot in front of the other!

The tracks of dinosaurs are not uncommonly preserved as either casts or moulds within the Purbeck and occasionally Wealden strata. Spotting them is challenging

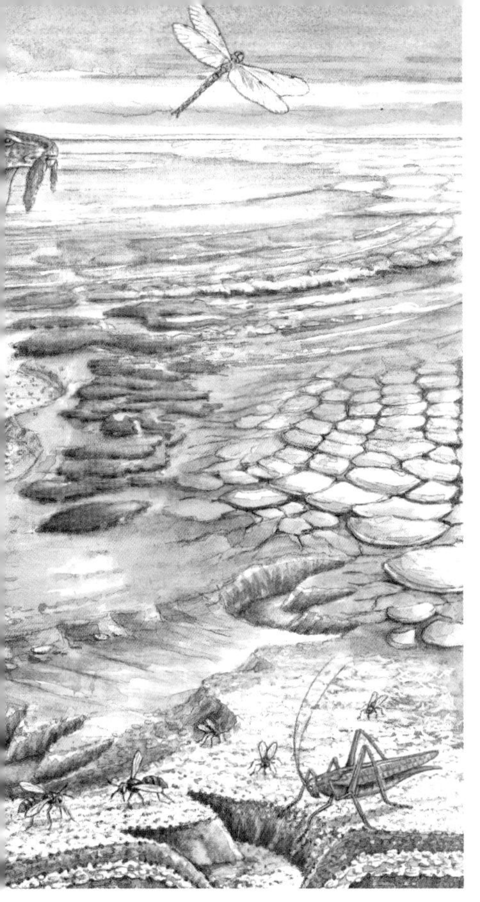

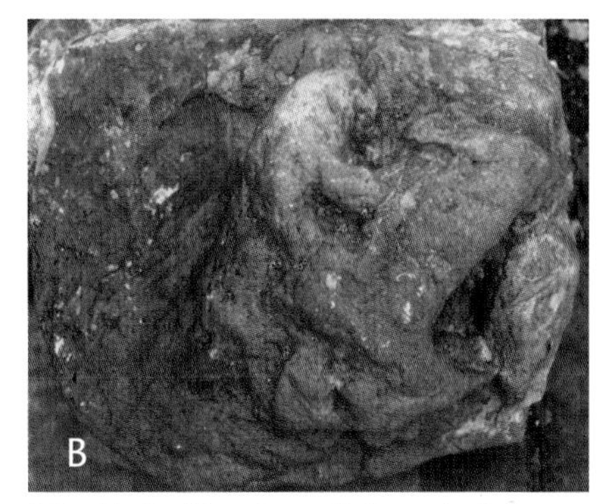

Fallen blocks of limestone with the casts of dinosaur tracks preserved.

A. Two consecutive tracks, arrowed, of a trackway.

B. Two superimposed tracks of different trackways going in opposite directions!

and best attempted when there is a low, raking light over exposed bedding planes. In recent years, many new records have been made, and such is the density of these remarkable fossils that the Isle of Purbeck may be regarded as a megatrack site. Identifying the dinosaurs which left the tracks is difficult, but we are aware of tracks belonging to both bipedal and quadrupedal dinosaurs. Rare teeth and bones are found and, in the last fifteen years, tiny pieces of the eggshell of these ruling reptiles have also been discovered.

Lying within these strata is the Jurassic–Cretaceous boundary, the subject of much debate over many decades. The ammonites which abound in most of the marine sequences, and which are so important for defining boundaries, are sadly lacking from these essentially non-marine strata. In their absence, microscopic plant remains and freshwater algae called charophytes have been used to assist in the definition of this elusive boundary. The presence of echinoids, scallops and barnacles, and even the rare remains of ichthyosaurs (p. 92) and plesiosaurs in some beds, give a tantalising hint that the sea may not have been so far away.

The mineral constituents of the clays and shales, and the fossils of the Purbeck strata, tell of an erratic transition from an early, strongly seasonal climate when deposits of evaporites were laid down during arid summers, to a more humid climate with increasing rainfall later in the period. There is evidence for periodic returns to aridity during this transition; average temperatures were 15°C compared to 9.8–12°C today. Four beds of clay within the Purbeck strata have compositions consistent with their being the product of volcanic ash falls.

Previously the Purbeck Limestone Group was mined, but today with the advent of powerful machinery it is extensively quarried for the many beautiful building and decorative stones present across the Isle of Purbeck. Among these is the snail-rich Purbeck Marble, which was much sought after for use in England's great medieval cathedrals, such as Salisbury, Lincoln and York.

This tiny sculpted body is the cast of the nucule of a charophyte and measures around 0.5mm in diameter. Charophytes (stoneworts) are freshwater algae which are calcified. They are common in some horizons of the Purbeck Limestone Group and are taken to indicate freshwater conditions.

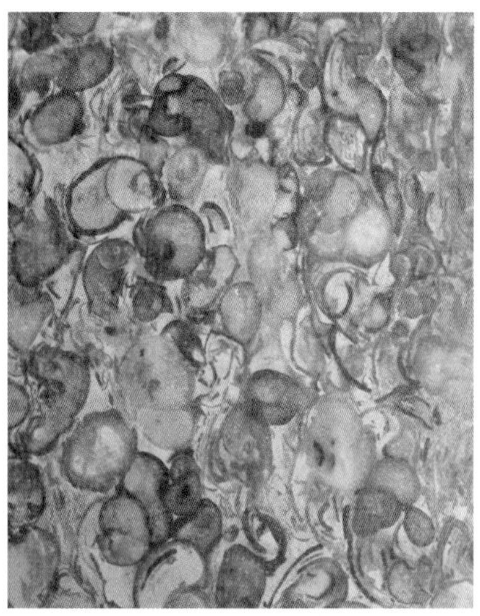

Purbeck Marble: the famed snail-rich limestone, which can be cut and polished, has found favour for use in everyday objects and in buildings, including some of our great cathedrals, since Roman times.

Braided Rivers and Shifting Channels: The Wealden Group, 136.8–124.8 Ma

With the Wealden we see the conclusion of the progressive transition from marine to terrestrial conditions that had started at the close of the Portland Group. While during the deposition of the succeeding Purbeck Limestone Group a 'whiff of the sea' had remained, this was now completely blown away. The grits, sands, silts and clays which make up this geological formation are present sporadically along the coast from near Ringstead (p. 43) to Swanage Bay (p. 96). At Dungy Head (p. 50) the Wealden is 65m thick, in Worbarrow Bay (p. 51) 366m, and at Swanage around 700m. Their vibrant reds and oranges, yellows and whites contribute a 'sands of Alum Bay' quality to those bits of Dorset where they are exposed. The clays are used locally for brick-making.

Wealden sediments across southern England were deposited over approximately 12 million years. They are represented by two formations, the Wessex and the Vectis – the latter from the Roman name for the Isle of Wight. In Dorset the Wessex Formation forms the bulk of the sequence, and the Vectis Formation is a rapidly thinning slither, just present in Swanage Bay but absent in Worbarrow Bay. The Wessex Formation represents an environment dominated by rivers, the Vectis Formation one dominated by lakes or lagoons, which on the Isle of Wight increasingly demonstrate the influence of the returning sea, after an absence of over 20 million years.

Wealden Group (Wessex Formation), Swanage Bay, which are frequently varicoloured clays, silts and sands. The reds and purples are characteristic of terrestrial deposits.

The rivers were fed by intermittent torrential rains, sweeping coarse grit with occasional pebbles, sand, silt and mud in a series of shifting channels which formed braided rivers. Their source was an eroding land mass to the west, over what is now Devon, Cornwall and into the South West Approaches, an area known as Cornubia. The sediments show that the granites of south-west England were exposed and contributing to the sediments. Plant-debris beds are present, thought to have formed when the rain-soaked and poorly consolidated sediments, with burnt vegetation resulting from wildfires sparked by lightning, created lethal sludge flows, entombing dinosaurs and other creatures. The bones and tracks of dinosaurs and pieces of resin are occasionally found. One location provides evidence of an oil seep active at the time.

The Returning Sea: The Lower Greensand Group, 124.8–107.3 Ma

While the Wealden provides the first hint of a returning sea, rare ammonites in the Lower Greensand near Swanage are the sure-fire indicator that after around 20 million years the sea was again starting to take control. The formation is believed to be over 80m thick in Swanage Bay (p. 96), but when traced westwards becomes thinner and devoid of ammonites, finally disappearing close to Lulworth Cove (p. 51): exposures at this western end have yielded molluscs of a distinctly Wealden type. One suggestion is that the Wealden river system was still present in the west, flowing eastwards through marshes, swamps, lagoons and an estuary before reaching the open sea. The estuary's influence appears to have waxed – reaching as far as the Isle of Wight – and waned over time. The abundance of pieces of fossil wood and a pebble bed in the strata in Swanage Bay all suggest that land was still close by. The Lower Greensand Group consists of sands, silts, clays and minor limestones, which are sometimes pebbly, and occasionally fossiliferous.

The global rise in sea level began in the late lower and early middle Cretaceous, reaching a maximum in the upper Cretaceous. It was connected to the formation of mid-ocean ridges, part of the process which led to the development of our modern oceans, including the Atlantic. As mid-ocean ridge formation took place, the rate of sea-floor spreading appears to have diminished. The mismatch between ridge development and sea-floor spreading led to the displacement of sea water and the progressive flooding of the land masses. A global rise or fall in sea level is known as a eustatic change, differing from isostatic adjustment caused by local uplift or subsidence.

With the Lower Greensand, we need to envisage the sea encroaching gradually on to an eroded landscape, one which had been tilted from west to east, a process which was also linked to the development of the Atlantic. In the following sections the continuation of this is documented, with the Gault and the Upper Greensand formations. The peak in the rise in sea level was reached around 35 million years after the deposition of the Lower Greensand, when the Chalk was being laid down over virtually the whole of Britain.

Muddy Sands: The Gault Formation, 107.3–102.7 Ma

After the Lower Greensand was deposited, the sea encroached further to the west, reaching into Devon. The Gault Formation resulted. While this may sound straightforward, the overall picture is more complex. The cliffs east of Ringstead (p. 43) and exposures inland demonstrate that Jurassic and early Cretaceous strata had been folded and eroded before the Gault was deposited unconformably. The Lower Greensand Group is missing west of Lulworth (p. 51) and, as previously noted, evidence points to none having been deposited. The juxtaposition of eroded folds and overlying unfolded strata is stark evidence that Earth movements and erosion occurred in this area some time towards the end of, or after, the deposition of the Wealden – and before the Gault sea encroached over this Cretaceous landscape. Despite much research connected with the prospecting for oil and gas in south Dorset, the sequence of events that led to this is still not fully understood. While not universally accepted, there is good reason to believe that the Wealden and some, or all, of the Purbeck Limestone Group sediments were not deposited north of the line of the Chalk ridgeway to the north of Swanage (p. 96) and Corfe Castle. However, we do know that they were deposited north of this axis in the west around Ringstead.

The lowest Gault strata are pebbly, providing tangible evidence for a period of erosion – as does a modern beach – followed in this case by transgression as the sea level rose. Above this, there are approximately 20m and 35m of clayey silts and sands,

The cliffs east of Ringstead reveal the dramatic events which took place before the Gault sea, encroaching from east to west, lapped on to an already faulted, folded and eroded land mass seen below the unconformity. This gap in deposition represents approximately 37 million years. Subsequently the unconformity and associated strata were tilted.

usually dark blue-black in colour and increasingly rich in glauconite. Glauconite is a distinctive mineral which ranges in colour from a green-black through light green to blue-green. Hard nodules or doggers of grey-black, fine-grained sandstone are present and may be fossiliferous. Bivalves, among which a small oyster called *Exogyra* is especially common, and ammonites, brachiopods and echinoids all occur. The small, coiled, calcareous tubes of a worm are sometimes abundant. The passage into the Upper Greensand Formation is marked by a blue-coloured sandy clay.

Shallow Water Sandstones: The Upper Greensand Formation, 102.7–99 Ma

Overlying the Gault come increasingly sandy sediments, where grains of the mineral glauconite are a sufficiently important component to impart a striking green colour to parts of the succession. The decrease in clay is reflected in the increasingly well-cemented sands and occasional development of chert bands.

As during the deposition of the preceding Gault, these strata accumulated as sea levels rose, gradually lapping on to and over western Dorset and east Devon. The coarser sandy sediments were being derived from the exposed areas to the west in Devon and beyond. These encroached eastwards into the progressively more muddy Gault sea. The Upper Greensand never reached as far east as Kent, where sediments of equivalent age are clays of the Gault Formation. Along this section of the Dorset coast, the Upper Greensand is thickest at Worbarrow Bay (p. 51), where approximately 23m are present.

The unconformable and mineralised contact (arrowed) between the Upper Greensand Formation and the Chalk Group, seen in a fallen block in Worbarrow Bay. The green colour is caused by the mineral glauconite, which forms in shallow water where little or no sediment is being deposited.

During the deposition of the Upper Greensand and lower beds of the Chalk across central Dorset, including parts of the coast, there were further movements of the rocks buried beneath this Cretaceous sea. These have pronounced local effects, with beds missing and distinctive unconformities. There are sometimes concentrations of phosphatised ammonites and other fossils. Bivalve fossils such as oysters and scallops are particularly common, but there are also echinoids and rare crustaceans. Even less common are shark's teeth. Extremely rare dinosaur bones have been found along the Dorset coast, one in Swanage Bay – hinting at land not so far away.

Coccolith Ooze: The Chalk Group, 99–65 Ma

Albion, the ancient name for Britain, was coined in recognition of the precipitous white cliffs along parts of England's southern and eastern coasts: Dorset is well endowed! For generations of geologists, the Chalk of the UK appeared in publications and on maps divided into the Lower, Middle and Upper Chalk. Detailed studies in the last few decades, some driven by the need for a better understanding of the Chalk for major engineering projects such as the Channel Tunnel and related rail links, have revealed a much greater degree of complexity 'hidden' within. The simple tripartite division has been replaced by the Chalk Group, which is divided into lower Grey Chalk and upper White Chalk subgroups. These are then divided into formations and members, named after the localities where they are best exposed and were described. The Chalk is a marine deposit laid down over some 30 million years. For the sake of simplicity, we have maintained the old tripartite division here, but show the new terminology in the diagram on page 15.

A casual glance at the Chalk suggests a uniform deposit of white limestone, composed of microscopic plants and animals, including their droppings, which rained down on to the sea floor. Water depths are thought to have been no greater than 300m. Closer examination reveals that the Chalk varies greatly in hardness, often develops regular banding, has beds where irregular nodular white Chalk is surrounded by wispy darker marls, surfaces that have been planed off and then buried, and bands of tabular or nodular flint. The raw material from which flint forms is high concentrations of silica in the sediment, produced by the dissolution of silica-rich organisms such as radiolarians and sponges. The precipitation of the silica is triggered in the sediments when hydrogen sulphide rising through the sediment undergoes a chemical change, releasing hydrogen. The hydrogen lowers

White Nothe looking to the north-west. In the middle distance the eroding toe of old landslips. In the foreground, the darker-coloured Upper Greensand Formation at the base of White Nothe is overlain by the rhythmically banded Chalk Group. Near-vertical cracks are NW–SE-orientated joints which are being enlarged by the action of the sea.

the sediment's pH, calcite is dissolved and the carbonate ions trigger flint formation. Tabular flints often resulted. Many of the flint nodules seen are the fossilised remains of burrows which preferentially allowed the migration of hydrogen sulphide and were fossilised selectively.

The regular banding seen in the Chalk and referred to above (p. 35) has been linked to the variation in energy levels from the sun caused by the clockwork-like changes in the axial tilt and inherited wobble of our planet. Even the regular bands of flints have been linked to these effects through climate change.

When analysed, these features reveal a complex underlying tectonic history. The Chalk oozes were not always laid down as uniform layers. They were swept from sea floors which had been gently warped by movements of buried structures, and accumulated in depressions; occasionally slumping took place. Periodically the sea-floor oozes became sufficiently consolidated for animals to create complex burrow systems within them, which have in turn been turned to flint. Flint is known to have formed relatively soon after the sediments were deposited. Sea floors were occasionally lithified to form hardgrounds. The darker sediments are either clay- and silt-sized particles washed in from the few remaining land masses, or volcanic ashes called bentonites.

The Chalk is often rich in the fossilised remains of the creatures which lived at the time.

After the Dinosaurs: The Cenozoic, 65 Ma to the Present Day

The uppermost part of the Chalk is missing from Dorset, though fossils found in 54–36 million year old gravel deposits on the top of the Chalk ridgeway north of

The view of the Chalk cliffs from Middle Beach, Studland. In the middle distance is Redend Point, which is composed of sandstones of the Poole Formation. There is an ongoing debate concerning the nature of the contact of the Cenozoic with the Cretaceous Chalk, the traditional unconformity with the Reading Formation filling an eroded Chalk surface, or as recently proposed, a faulted contact with the Poole Formation.

Dolines, also known as solution holes, in the cliffs of St Oswald's Bay. The sediments in these features are thought to be of Neogene age but may incorporate much older Paleogene sediments.

Weymouth do suggest that some of this uppermost Chalk was deposited over Dorset. The more easterly part of the coast covered by this guide does reveal sediments that were deposited over an eroded Chalk surface. To the west, exposed in the cliff at St Oswald's Bay (p. 50), there are sediments preserved in dolines (p. 37). These could be as old as 2.65 million years, and may even incorporate deposits up to 54 million years old. In the absence of firm dating evidence, this is pure speculation.

To the north of the ridgeway and exposed in Studland Bay are clays, sands and gravels which may belong to the Reading and London Clay formations (see pp. 16–17) and the Poole Formation. Deposits of ball clay, laid down as flood-plain deposits within these strata, are of considerable economic importance for the ceramics industry, and there are many disused mines and actively worked opencast pits scattered across the heathlands. The clays of this age have yielded beautifully preserved plant fossils, rare insects and even a shark's tooth.

The deposits that rest unconformably on the Chalk downs fall into both older, as noted above, and younger categories. They are the products of erosion and dissolution of existing rocks. The younger ones date from the last 2.65 Ma and are known by names such as 'Clay-with-Flints', 'Head' and alluvium, deposits which formed during the Pleistocene – the period of time thought of as the Ice Age. In fact, this episode has been punctuated by often rapid fluctuations in temperature and precipitation. There have been several glaciations, one of which reached as far south as London. The continuing evolution of the landscape is dramatically illustrated by both dormant and active landslides and rockslides, which are present around the coast. Good examples are seen at White Nothe (p. 50), Flower's Barrow (p. 51) and St Aldhelm's Head (p. 77), and below Ballard Down (p. 96).

Rocks and Wildlife

Any geologist studying the rocks of the Jurassic Coast can't fail to notice the area's wealth of wildlife, and this is particularly true in the Isle of Purbeck. Much of this rich diversity is the result of different types of underlying rock producing a wide variety of soils and ground conditions. The Chalk downland of Ballard Down, the limestone grassland of the Purbeck cliffs and the heathlands of Studland are classic examples of this. All have distinctive soils that support a flora, which in turn attracts particular species of animals. In spring and summer the cliff tops display a remarkable collection of wild flowers, birds, mammals, reptiles, butterflies, moths and many other insects.

Between St Aldhelm's head and Durlston, a noticeable feature is the 'Prickle Bed' or 'Puffin Ledge'. The softer shale band has been eroded out, leaving a prominent ledge and shelter for nesting seabirds.

Kittiwakes make good use of irregular ledges at Blacker's Hole in the Portland Limestone cliffs.

But this is only part of the story, because the physical characteristics of the rocks are also important, particularly where they outcrop along the coast. In Swanage and Worbarrow Bays, for example, the largely unconsolidated Wealden sediments form unstable cliffs which are not conducive to colonisation by wildlife. At Ballard Cliff and along the Purbeck cliffs, however, the much harder Chalk and Portland Limestone form towering cliffs, which are not only relatively stable, but also contain a multitude of nooks, crannies and ledges, which are colonised by plants and animals. Seabirds, such as herring and great black-backed gulls, kittiwakes, cormorants, shags, guillemots, razorbills and small numbers of puffins, thrive here, and increasingly so do ravens and peregrine falcons.

The influence of the geology doesn't stop at the water's edge. Underwater hard rock outcrops are particularly important in forming reefs, which are rich in wildlife. The best reefs can be seen in the Kimmeridge Marine Reserve, along the coastal stretch from Kimmeridge to Chapman's Pool, off Ringstead Bay and around the stumps of old Chalk stacks near Old Harry Rocks and into Studland Bay (pp. 116–17).

Wildlife of the Jurassic Coast by Bryan Edwards takes a detailed look at the relationship between geology and wildlife along the World Heritage Site. Lavishly illustrated, this is one of a series of publications by the Jurassic Coast Trust.

THE ITINERARY

Introduction to the Coastal Sections

In the last chapter we described in sequence, and some detail, the rocks and the geological history of the area. It is now time to explore the coast and take a closer look at the rocks themselves and at the landscapes within which they lie.

The coast has been divided into convenient sections, each with a short introduction that includes maps showing footpaths and car-parking areas. Information on access is provided and there is a short summary of highlights to look out for. Within each section, annotated photographs help to explain the geology and show how it relates to coastal features and landscapes.

In addition, there are eight special sections that describe themes or subjects of special interest. Along some parts of the Purbeck coast the cliffs drop sheer into the sea – there are no beaches – so we have included two double pages describing the coast as you can see it from a boat. Boat trips are available in season, weather permitting, from Poole, Swanage, Lulworth Cove and Weymouth.

Furzy Cliff to White Nothe

To the west of Bowleaze Cove the beach is sandy; to the east it contains pebbles and becomes increasingly rocky. The beaches can be accessed on foot from the west of Furzy Cliff, at Bowleaze Cove, Osmington Mills and Ringstead Bay. There are no visitor centres within this section, but interpretation panels can be seen at the principal access points.

This section is of relatively low relief with cliffs subject to landslides in many places. Highlights include large spherical doggers, oolitic limestones, fossil burrows, sands smelling of oil, an angular unconformity, a massive landslide and the 'Burning Cliff'.

The profile of Furzy Cliff, captured by John Constable in his painting of 1816, (p. 44) has not changed greatly. The housing developments atop Jordan Hill and Overcombe, manicured, neat and tucked to the west and north, the last settlement on the south-eastern edge of the Weymouth lowlands, are recent. Jordan Hill's seaward extension forms Furzy Cliff, which has fortunately escaped the concrete-cladding of sea defences such as those stretching from Weymouth to Preston and at Bowleaze Cove. The clays of the Oxford Clay Formation, the oldest strata described in this guide, are still washed by the sea, slipping and slumping their way to the beach. Well-preserved fossils, which have included a rare starfish and the skeletons of extinct marine reptiles, are found frequently. Particularly common are those in red-coloured nodules weathered from the clays. The strata dip down to the north and east, and as traced eastwards towards Bowleaze Cove the cliff diminishes in size and becomes increasingly overgrown.

The view from White Nothe to the west along cliffs cut in the folded and faulted strata of the northern limb of the Weymouth Anticline. In the foreground is the complex landslipped area below White Nothe.

Jordan Hill with Furzy Cliff below, painted by John Constable in 1816.

Between the sea defences east of Bowleaze Cove and just east of Redcliff Point, the Corallian Group, which follows the Oxford Clay, appears to form a shallow saucer-shaped deposit of tough sandstones, clays and limestones. At Redcliff Point, a fault juxtaposes the Oxford Clay against the Corallian and then just east of the point, at Ham Cliff, a small anticline sees the topmost parts of the Oxford Clay emerging from below sea level to form the cliff.

The strata along these cliffs look a bit like a switchback. First they plunge down eastwards beneath Black Head, to rise again towards Osmington Mills. Here the upward sweep of the strata is broken by faults, before gradually descending along the cliff to Bran Point and beyond.

At Black Head, the Kimmeridge Clay Formation is present on the flanks of the great tumbled slip (slips can be extremely hazardous and should not be climbed on or over at any time) which cascades younger Cretaceous sediments shorewards. It was near here that the 2.4m–long skull and jaws of the pliosaur, now on display in the Dorset County Museum, which hit the headlines in 2009, were recovered over a period

A rare starfish fossil from the Oxford Clay, with a diameter of about 6cm.

of several years. Apart from the specimen's considerable size, the large numbers of organisms which have encrusted it and the preservation of the bone provide valuable information on what happened to this monster once it had died. The toes of landslides are washed by the sea and sometimes lumps of fossiliferous grey-black and green sandstones from the Gault and Upper Greensand formations are exposed, yielding ammonites, bivalves and echinoids.

On 18 July 1955 Osmington Mills was a peripheral victim to a 'catastrophic event', the likes of which strike the UK from time to time. The 280mm of rain that fell on Martinstown a few miles to the north-west, as an area of thundery rain decayed more or less overhead, is the highest one day's (09.00–09.00) rainfall recorded anywhere in the UK. Over 180mm fell in just four and a half hours. (On 19 November 2009, Seathwaite in Cumbria received 316.4mm in the period 00.00–23.59.) While the most intense rainfall was very localised, the catchment area of the Osmington stream received substantially more rain than it would usually receive in months and became a raging torrent. The stream bed was deeply scoured and property was damaged. W.J. Arkell, describing the event and its consequences, reported that 'many tons of boulders and other debris [were swept] into the sea', with a delta forming across the shore. The evidence of catastrophic events is found in the geological record. An excellent local example is the sudden inundation by hypersaline waters of a forest near Lulworth 140 Ma (pp. 53–55).

From Osmington eastwards, the cliffs provide a fine section through the Corallian Group, which is composed variously of coarse sand, sand, clay and a variety of limestones. The lowest, the Redcliff Formation, is composed of the Nothe Grit

The 2.4m-long skull and jaws of a very large pliosaur from the Kimmeridge Clay Formation near Osmington.

Member – present in the cliffs at the foot of the Osmington stream valley – and the Preston Grit Member, over which the stream tumbles. Next are the Nothe Clay and Bencliff Grit members. Exposure improves as the cliff is followed. The Bencliff Grit is the source of the magnificent spherical-sub-spherical concretions, also known as doggers, which litter the shore. They show impressive examples of a distinctive form of cross-bedding, interpreted as the result of storms affecting a near-shore estuarine, or possibly lagoonal, deposit. These sediments contain plant material and microfossils indicative of fresh water; tellingly, the marine ammonites are absent.

In warm weather, some surfaces of the Bencliff Grit smell strongly of oil, thought to have originated from Lower Jurassic sediments some kilometres to the north. Here they had been buried sufficiently deeply for their organic content to be turned into oil, which then migrated southwards following porous and permeable strata. Since the mid-1930s, several exploratory oil wells have been drilled in the area both on- and offshore. The most recent was drilled by AMOCO from near Chaldon in 1997 to investigate a potential offshore oil-bearing structure, 'The Arkell Prospect', lying about 457m below sea level 1.5km offshore.

Next in the succession is the Osmington Oolite Formation. Among these beds are limestones made of tiny spheres (<1mm in diameter) of calcite called ooliths. Their resemblance to the coarse roe of a fish led to this name, the rock being named an oolite (pp. 20–21). Also present is a pisolite composed of rather gross-looking ooliths called pisoliths. They formed when algae trapped sediment in layers around a nucleus: they are around 10mm in diameter. Small echinoids are not uncommon, along with bivalves and gastropods. Throughout the Corallian strata, trace fossils are frequently seen. Here, in the top member, are the horizontal branching crustacean burrows that have become nodules.

Echinoid (*Pseudholaster*) from the Gault Formation near Osmington.

Another prominent bed is the Clavellata Member of the Clavellata Formation. On the foreshore, worn surfaces of this bed exhibit sections through the thick shells of the large and tuberculate marine bivalves *Myophorella clavellata*. They had evolved to withstand turbulent, shallow-water conditions on the sea floor.

East of Bran Point, the clay cliffs are frequently slumped with shingle banked against them. Exposures do provide glimpses of the Sandsfoot Formation. Occasionally corals are found in the latter, which was previously known as the Ringstead Coral Bed. This marks the junction of the Corallian with the Kimmeridge Clay, which is also present along this degraded cliff and toe of an immense area of ancient landslide. Scattered oyster shells (*Deltoideum delta*) are not uncommon and are worthy of careful examination, as the shells, before and after death, provided a firm substrate for attachment by a variety of other organisms, including tiny foraminifera, bryozoans and serpulids. A strange lopsided brachiopod called *Torquirhynchia inconstans* is occasionally found.

The combination of cliff instability, linked to significant changes in the beach profile during storm events, with the geological importance of the exposures has led to inevitable conflict between landowners and conservation groups. This came to a head in the late 1980s and 1990s. Over this time a range of protective work was undertaken, including the introduction of rock armour and a rock groyne and beach replenishment after the lowering of the beach by 1.5m during a series of storms, a reduction from which it had not recovered.

The Kimmeridge Clay succession at Ringstead Bay is significantly thinner than at Kimmeridge only 15km to the east. Why? Studies in the 1980s led to the conclusion that while the sea floor at Ringstead was able to accumulate organic-rich sediments and was therefore likely to have been at a similar depth to Kimmeridge, subsidence was slower and less sediment was accommodated. Sediments did include organic-rich shales, and in 1826, below Holworth House, these spontaneously ignited and burned for several years, lending the name Burning Cliff (p. 23), which still appears on the 1:25000 Ordnance Survey sheet of the area.

Doggers from the Bencliff Grit Member litter the shore just east of where the path from Osmington Mills descends to the beach. Inset shows a dogger exhibiting cross-bedding: the long lines roughly follow the contacts between the surfaces of the sand waves, the short lines show the attitude of the bedding within the different sand waves. (Scale bar = 10cm)

The cliffs immediately east of Burning Cliff provide a spectacular view of the dramatic events that took place before the Gault Formation was deposited. High on the cliffs, and seen in slipped masses at beach level, are strata of the Portland and Purbeck Limestone groups. They appear as a result of a north–south fault, active during the Cretaceous, with down-throw on the east side. After the folding, faulting and erosion had taken place, the Gault sea transgression progressively spread west, covering this area and forming a spectacular angular unconformity, which is overlain by the Gault and Upper Greensand formations and the Chalk Group. The unconformity is visible in the cliffs to the east of Ringstead Bay out to White Nothe (p. 33), now tilted from the near horizontal of the time by subsequent tectonic activity.

White Nothe looms large to the east of Ringstead Bay, providing a fine example of a complex area of landslides. These are of uncertain date, but may reasonably be expected to have originated during the last 14,000 years as the climate ameliorated at the close of the last cold period with glaciations, known as the Devensian.

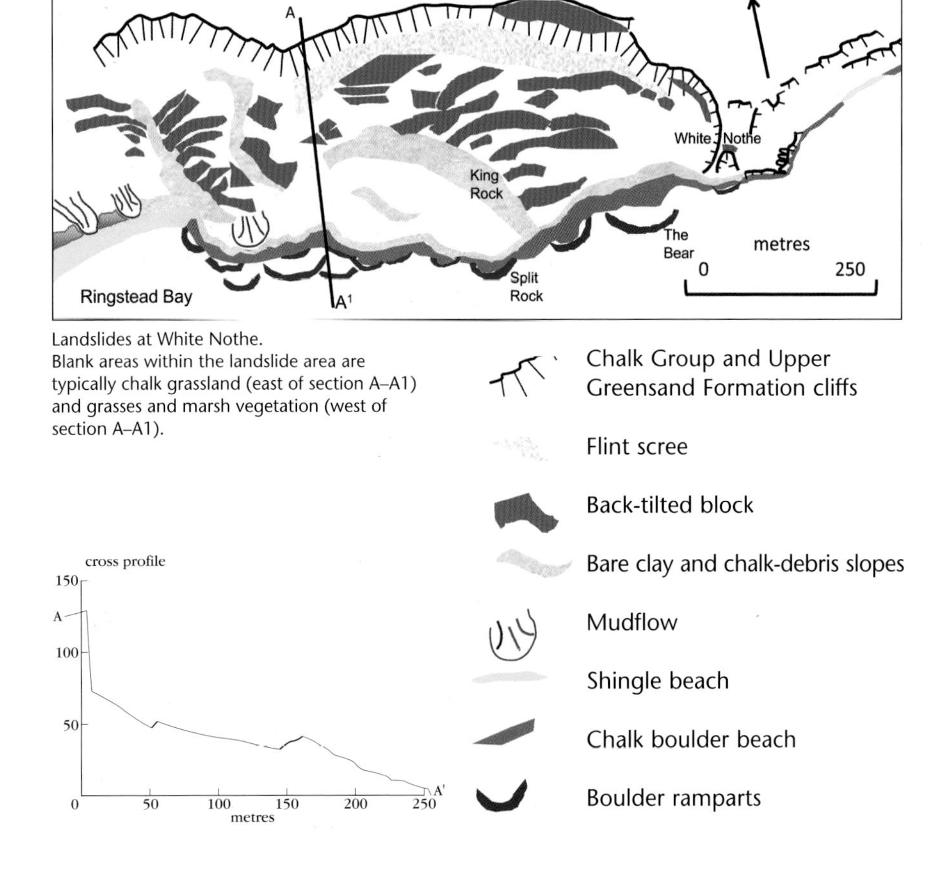

Landslides at White Nothe.
Blank areas within the landslide area are typically chalk grassland (east of section A–A1) and grasses and marsh vegetation (west of section A–A1).

White Nothe viewed from above 'Burning Cliff', Ringstead. The angular unconformity at the base of the Gault Formation is visible along with the major landslides below White Nothe.

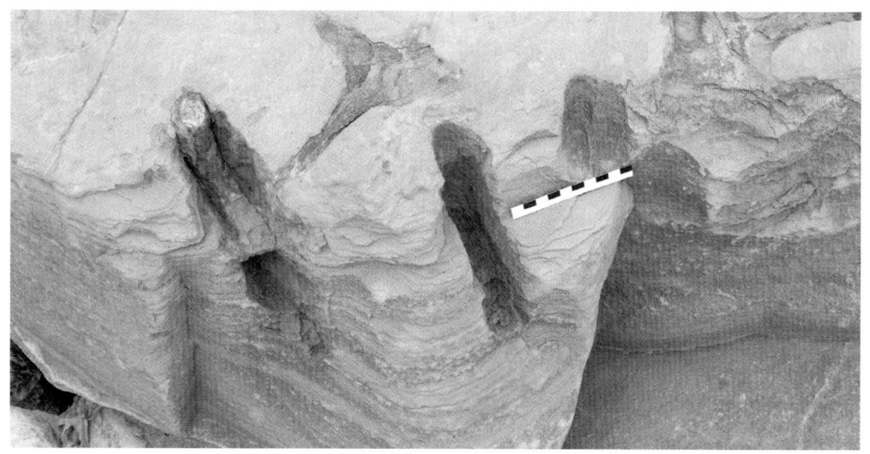

U-shaped vertical burrows called diplocraterion. The burrow was backfilled and migrated upwards as sediment was deposited, or downwards if the sea floor was being eroded (scale bar shown 10cm).

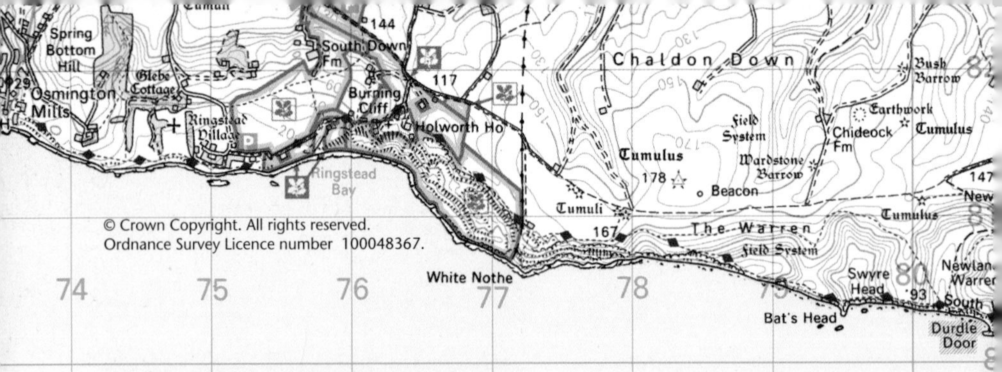

White Nothe to Worbarrow Tout

Sandy beaches can be accessed from Durdle Door, Lulworth Cove, Mupe Bay and Tyneham village – the latter two are within the MoD firing ranges and are only open when the ranges are open to the public (opening times are normally available at the Lulworth Visitor Centre or by telephoning 01929 462721). There is no car parking at Mupe Bay, which can only be accessed from the South West Coast Path. There are a number of World Heritage interpretation panels and the large Visitor Centre at Lulworth contains excellent geological information. Historical information is available at Tyneham. Boat trips to Worbarrow Tout are recommended.

The section is characterised by superb Chalk cliffs, and highlights include a magnificent coastal arch, sheltered coves, 'crumpled' cliffs, a fossil forest, dinosaur tracks and blocks of gypsum.

Spectacularly different from the cliffs described so far, the cliffs between the aptly named White Nothe and Worbarrow Tout form a rarely perforated bastion against the erosive power of the sea, with the limestones of the Portland, Purbeck Limestone and Chalk groups lying at differing angles of repose.

The range of landscape features along this section of coast (pp. 59–67) is the result of a subtle interplay between the rocks of varying hardness, the forces to which they have been exposed and the resultant structures, the landscape which subsequently developed and the effects of changes in sea level on that landscape. Over the last 65 million years, the once almost horizontal rocks exposed along this coast have been subjected to an important episode of folding which tilted them more or less steeply. These hugely stressful processes fractured the rocks, forming the intricate patterns of joints that may be seen criss-crossing exposed surfaces today. The folded strata, with their inherited lines of weakness, have played a crucial role in the subsequent evolution of the coast.

The Chalk emerges from the landslides discussed in the previous section and is best seen from the sea. At sea level the lowest Chalk rests on the darker Upper Greensand Formation. Where exposed to the full force of the sea, pronounced banding is seen in the former (p. 35), probably related to astronomical cycles. At White Nothe the strata dip at a modest 5 degrees in an east-south-easterly direction. From here increasingly precipitous Chalk cliffs predominate. These are cut by steep-sided dry valleys, which are in turn truncated by the sea. Chalk solifluction deposits, modern glacial and interglacial deposits, are often present in the valley bottoms. Walking east

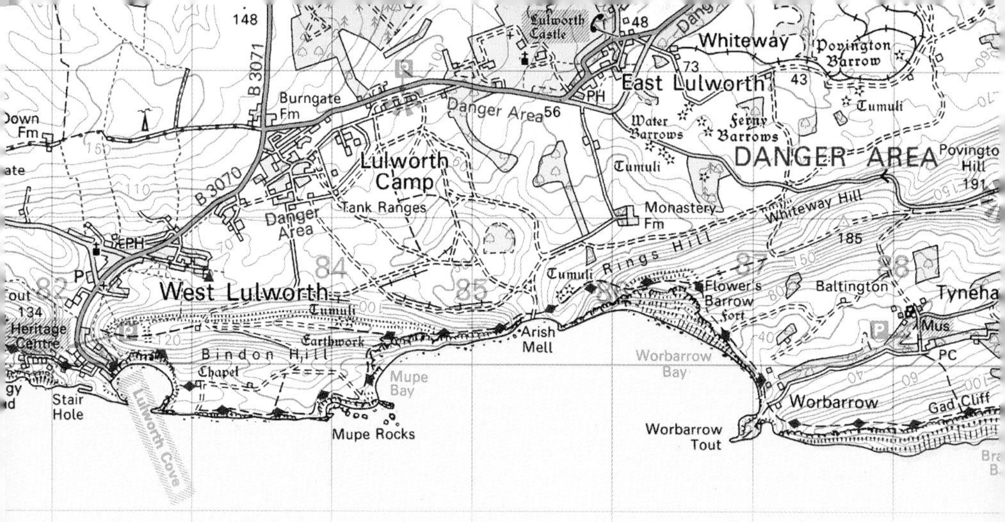

along the cliff-top path, the axis of the Purbeck Monocline's foresyncline is crossed just west of Bat's Head, and from there the Chalk is almost vertical and in the cliffs at Man o' War Head west of Dungy Head is overturned. A series of small caves has formed along the plane of a low-angle fault in the Chalk between Bat's Head and Swyre Head (p.63).

Just south of Bat's Head, there are visible vestiges of the Portland Stone Formation protruding as offshore rocks known as the The Calf, The Cow and The Bull. These may mark the remains of storm-and-gravity defying arches, a fantastic example of

The Blind Cow (left) and The Bull (right), relics of the Portland Sone barrier

Durdle Door – a natural arch cut through the almost-vertical Portland Stone Formation

Purbeck Limestone and Wealden groups

Aerial view from above the Fossil Forest looking west towards White Nothe. The position of the strata, major structural features and key locations are identified.

which is seen as the outcrop of Portland strata is followed eastwards, rearing from the sea as a vertical and curtain-like sheet of stone to form the cliff and great natural arch of Durdle Door (p. 60). Based on the etymology of the name, the arch is known to have stood for at least 800 years and quite possibly over 1,000 years.

Traced eastwards, the Portland Stone Formation (p. 24) forms both submerged reefs and the resilient and protective cliff line as far east as the west end of Gad Cliff. At the same time, the dip of these strata alters from near vertical to a steep northerly direction; in the far distance the same strata capping St Aldhelm's Head can be seen dipping at a very low angle to the south (p. 73). This dramatic variation in the steepness and direction of dip is a consequence of the coast's position relative to the axis of the Purbeck Monocline, which follows the line of the Chalk ridgeway (pp. 16–17). The submerged rock ledges and reefs which trace the positions of the former barriers are visible on side-scan sonar and provide valuable clues to the development of these coastal features (pp. 116–117). These barriers also provide an important control on the supply and removal of beach sediments from the bays and coves.

Where a weakness in the Portland Stone barrier exists it is exploited. Stair Hole with the alarming crumple, a gravity-induced slide within the steeply inclined strata of the Purbeck Limestone Group, is an early stage in the formation of a new cove. However, there can be little dissent that the most famous result of a 'weakness' in the Portland Stone barrier along this coast is the iconic Lulworth Cove. This geomorphological wonder has thrown up challenges for those trying to explain its origin (see pp. 60–67).

The cove has been carved out from mostly soft Cretaceous sediments sandwiched between the Jurassic Portland Stone on the seaward side and the back wall of Cretaceous Chalk. Between these two thicker limestones are the clays, shales and thin limestones of the Purbeck Limestone Group, the slumped sands and clays of the Wealden Group, a very thin deposit representing the Lower Greensand Group, and the Gault and Upper Greensand formations. The youngest strata, apart from the debris of the last 10,000 years, are those of the relatively resilient Chalk at the back of the cove.

Artist's reconstruction of the Fossil Forest based on a detailed study of the fossil trees from the Purbeck Limestone Group undertaken by Professor Jane Francis for her PhD in the 1980s.

Caution: if using the narrow, fringing shingle beach, beware of falling debris as small pieces and much larger chunks of the cliff can and do fall without warning.

East from Lulworth Cove (p. 65) the Portland Stone Formation forms a buttress to the sea and is capped by the basal Purbeck strata. These limestones, formed from stromatolites, were accumulating in shallow and very salty water along the shores of a Purbeck lagoon. Coniferous trees, specially adapted to this harsh environment of hot arid summers, fringed the lagoon. The sediment-filled crystals of halite (salt pseudomorphs) are evidence of the once-arid conditions that existed. Periodically, movement along east–west faults caused these 'forests' to be swamped, killing the trees and leading to their trunks and branches being entombed by the stromatolites. The stromatolite 'bowls' are seen in the Fossil Forest (p. 53), perched atop the buttress, though the fossil wood is long gone.

Bacon Hole (p. 107), so called because of the Purbeck strata's resemblance to rashers of streaky bacon (some suggest the smell from smugglers feasting on bacon as an alternative!), provides a fine section through these strata where occasional dinosaur tracks have been found. The stromatolites of the lowest strata become a rarity, though the finest sediments laid down may owe their origins in part to the continuing existence, and relatively close proximity, of these sediment-producing stromatolites. Close to the top of the succession, small-scale mounding algal stromatolites are once again present.

The Fossil Forest near Lulworth Cove. Stromatolites, complex cyanobacterial colonies, formed the envelopes and mounds around the stumps and fallen trunks of conifers which fringed the Purbeck lagoon. The trees were periodically drowned when movement took place along one of the contemporary east–west trending faults. The petrified tree wood has long gone!

Mupe and Worbarrow Bays are part of a whole, sharing an almost unbroken Chalk cliff as a back wall. The most likely mode of formation is that the two bays originated independently and then coalesced, Worbarrow developing along the valleys through the Arish Mell gap and from Tyneham, whereas Mupe Bay, lacking a valley, resulted from a cave penetrating the outer Portland Group barrier. Another possibility is that a higher sea level flooded up the Arish Mell valley and the 'coalesced bays' resulted as the softer sediments of the Wealden and Lower Greensand groups and Gault and Upper Greensand formations fell prey to the power of the sea. The Wealden Group forms striking cliffs, which tell of flood plains with braided rivers and rare dinosaurs walking over them, and of floods that brought down masses of plant debris. Coarse iron oxide cemented grits provide evidence of sources to the west and north-west. The Lower

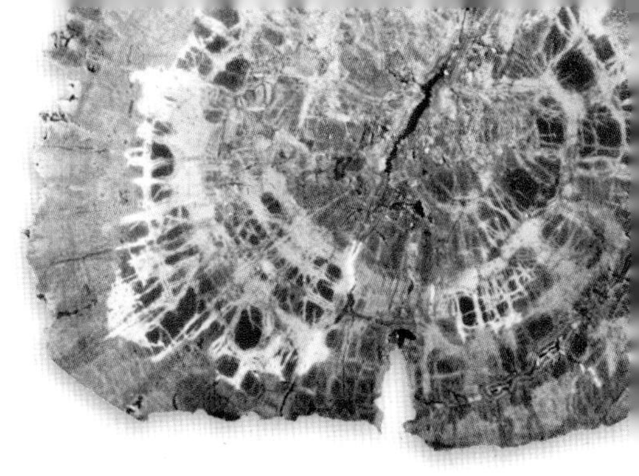

A cut and polished section through a piece of silicified wood. The concentric growth rings and radiating medullary rays are still visible.

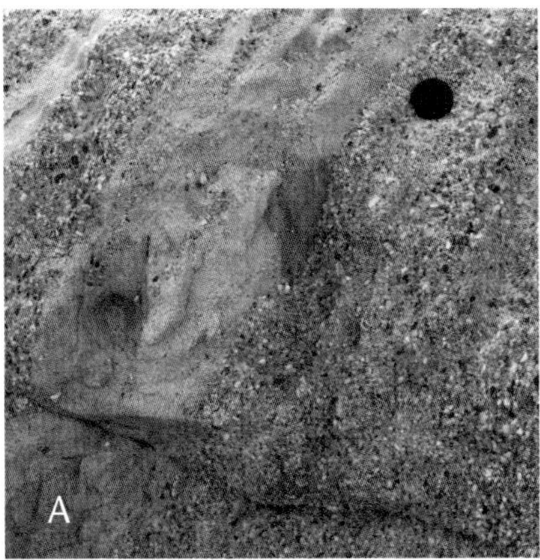

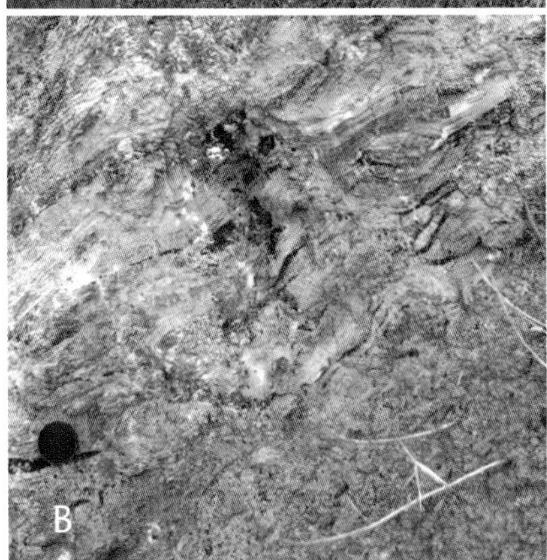

Wealden sediments: (A) coarse grits at the Durdle Door promontory; (B) plant-rich silty clays, Worbarrow Bay; and trace fossil (C), the cast of a rare tridactyl dinosaur track from Worbarrow Bay.

Greensand, predominantly marine to the east of Swanage, is interpreted here as swamp and brackish water environments, transitional between the Wealden Group and the marine Gault Formation.

Worbarrow Tout exposes a fine, though hazardous, section through the Purbeck Limestone Group. The section has yielded evidence of multiple dinosaur tracks in over 10 horizons, of earthquake activity at the time the sediments were being deposited, and in one bed a fragment of an upper Kimmeridge Clay ammonite was found, indicating penecontemporaneous erosion was occurring somewhere within the catchment area of these sediments. Evaporites are also present. Large blocks of gypsum with complex folded structures are present on the shore, there are horizons where calcite has replaced gypsum crystals, and the Broken Beds are believed to represent the collapse of the overlying strata into cavities left after evaporite deposits were dissolved and as the rocks were folded. Close to the base of these strata are finely laminated black shales in which the remains of tiny crustaceans called conchostracans are found. These provide evidence of a strongly seasonal climate; they were adapted to a reproductive cycle that took advantage of winter rains triggering

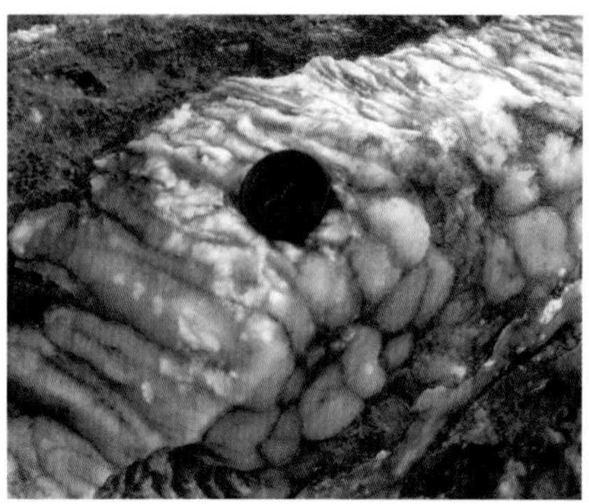

Intricately folded gypsum (enterolithic texture) is sometimes seen in fallen blocks on the shore of Worbarrow Tout. These represent ancient evaporite deposits.

The moderately chaotic Broken Beds in the lowest Purbeck Limestone Group are thought to have originated during Cenozoic folding when beds of limestone collapsed into the voids left after evaporite minerals had been dissolved. The small ruck-fold in the more coherent bed (arrowed) suggests a gravity collapse similar to those seen at Stair Hole.

the hatching of encysted eggs. Sexual maturity was reached and next season's eggs were laid before the ephemeral pools dried up.

Mupe and Worbarrow Bays are within the MoD firing ranges but accessible (when the ranges are open to the public) with relative ease from the South West Coast Path.

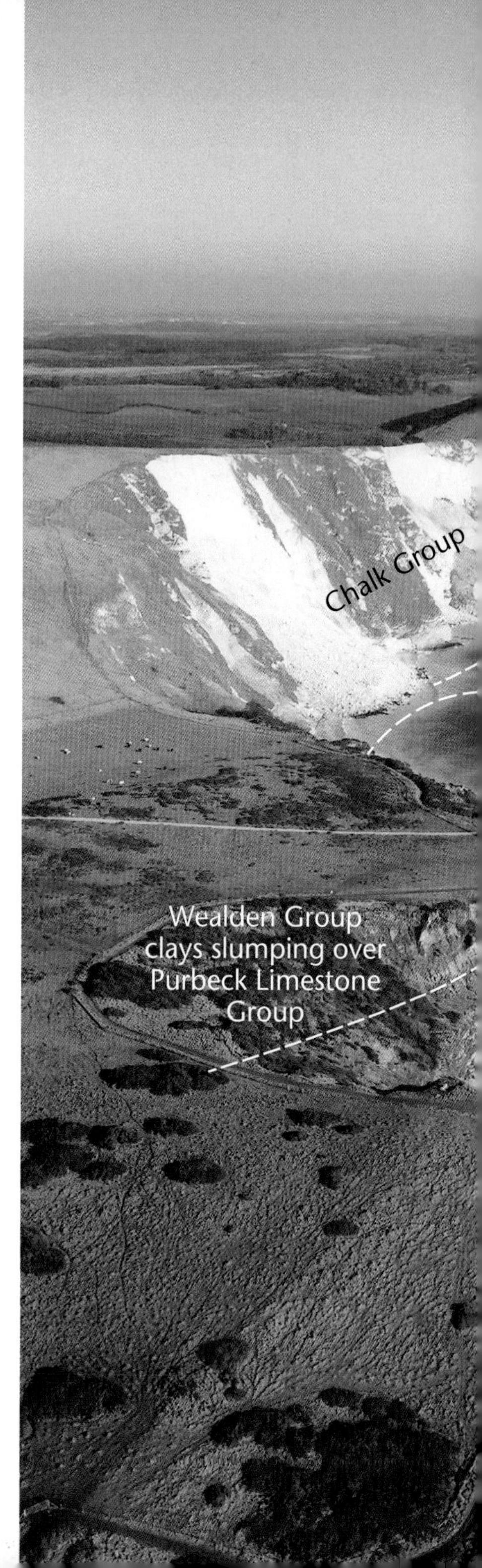

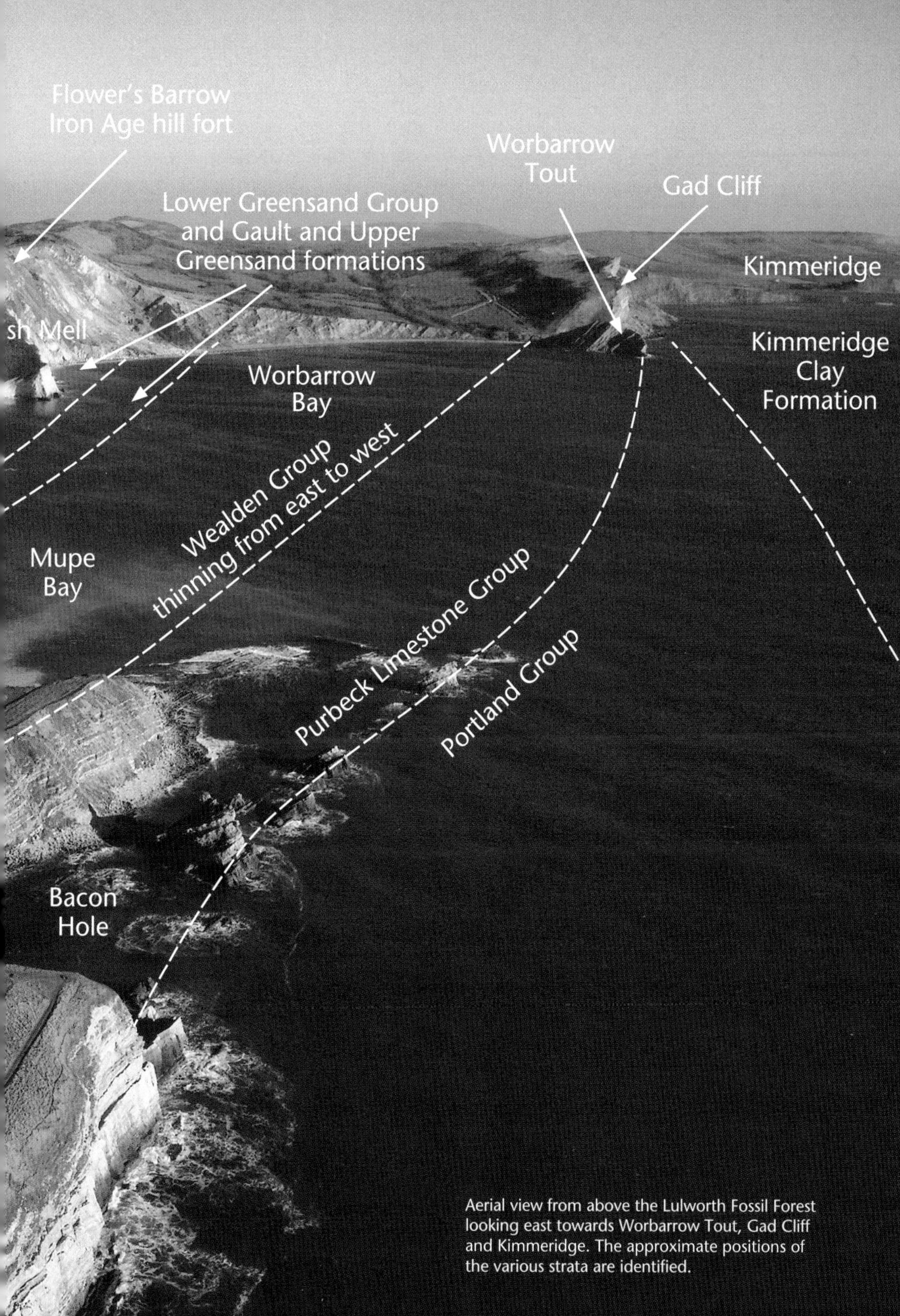

Aerial view from above the Lulworth Fossil Forest looking east towards Worbarrow Tout, Gad Cliff and Kimmeridge. The approximate positions of the various strata are identified.

Caves, Arches, Stacks, Coves and Landslides

The coast of the Isle of Purbeck is endowed with a remarkable range of geomorphological features which are closely related to the geology of the area. The coast remains the subject of rigorous study, providing many classic textbook examples of coastal landforms.

This coast demonstrates the intimate relationship between rock types with very different characters, their strength, their dip and strike, and the coastal landforms they underpin. The burial and diagenesis of the sediments, and the complex and dynamic history of faulting and folding, have provided a configuration of the strata, frequently with joints, which is now subjected to the ever-present agents of erosion. The strata's predominant direction of strike (east–west) and mostly northerly dip, from near vertical – sometimes overturned – to almost horizontal, along this coast is controlled by the Purbeck Monocline and the Weymouth and Purbeck anticlines (p. 61). The impact of these structures is seen in the way in which the strata outcrop along this coast and the way in which the landforms that make this coast internationally famous have developed. The coast of the Isle of Purbeck exhibits a fine longitudinal section from Worbarrow Tout east to Durlston Head, with transverse sections across Worbarrow Bay and north from Durlston Head in Durlston Bay (p. 80).

There are three rock types which exert a powerful control on erosion along this coast: the stone bands within the Kimmeridge Clay Formation (p. 73); the Portland Stone Formation, both *in situ* (p. 65) and influenced by its dip, and as boulder beaches (p. 71); and the Chalk where hardened by the tectonic processes to which it has been exposed.

Caves are present along this coast. They have formed where the sea exploits lines of weaknesses such as joints or faults. There are some small examples in Durdle Cove which have formed along a horizontal fault plane in the Chalk (p. 63). Further east, there are a number of caves in Portland and Purbeck strata, including Bacon Hole. The Tilly Whim Caves are disused and inaccessible stone mines (p. 85). There are further caves in the Chalk between Ballard Point and Old Harry (p. 96).

Arches, like caves, form when lines of weakness within a rock permit the sea to erode a hole. Both here and at The Needles, Isle of Wight, arches have formed where the strata are steeply inclined and softer sediment is reached. Durdle Door (p. 60) is especially famous, but other examples include Bat's Hole (p. 63), the perforation in the rock barrier at Stair Hole (p. 64), and several examples at Handfast Point, one in the headland itself and two in the large separated block, where the strata are near horizontal.

The stacks at Handfast Point are the final phase of the cave–arch–stack cycle. They are characteristic of the properties of the Chalk where the narrowing headland, combined with vertical joints and a more resistant Chalk stratum coinciding with sea level, have encouraged initial perforation to form caves and then arches. Preferential collapse of the vertical joints above the arches leads to stack formation. These, too, inevitably succumb to the constant attack of the sea and elements, as demonstrated by the sad loss of Old Harry's (earlier) wife in 1896. Fortunately for Old Harry, replacement wives have been created from time to time!

Early work on the development of coves and bays along the coast, from Bat's Head to Worbarrow Tout, suggested a simple evolutionary succession.

- Caves were initiated in steeply dipping Portland strata.
- The caves developed into arches when the overlying softer sediments on the landward side were washed away, as seen at Stair Hole (p. 64).
- The cove was enlarged by a combination of the sea and slumping of the unconsolidated sediment of the cliff during periods of heavy rainfall.
- The arch became unstable and collapsed, and the progressive destruction of the rock wall allowed the formation of a cove or bay.

Durdle Door. The derivation of the name points to a presence of at least 800 and possibly 1,000 years. Contrast the steep northerly dip of the Portland Stone of the arch with the same gently dipping strata which cap the Isle of Portland, on the southern limb of the Weymouth Anticline, in the distance.

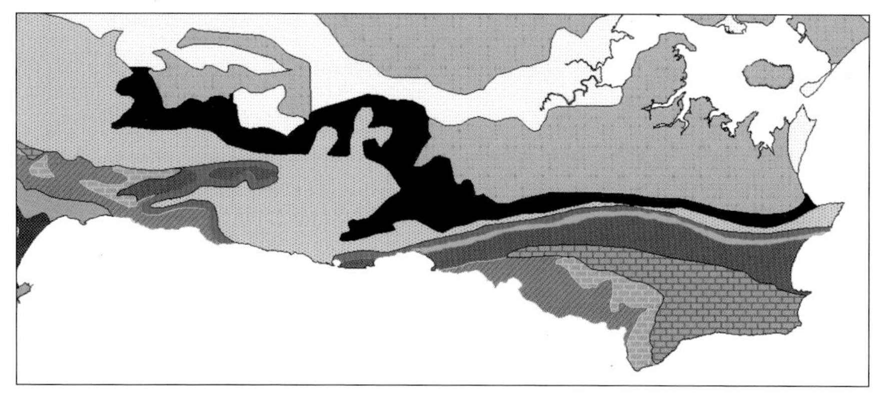

A. The geology of the area covered in this guide. See page 11 for key.

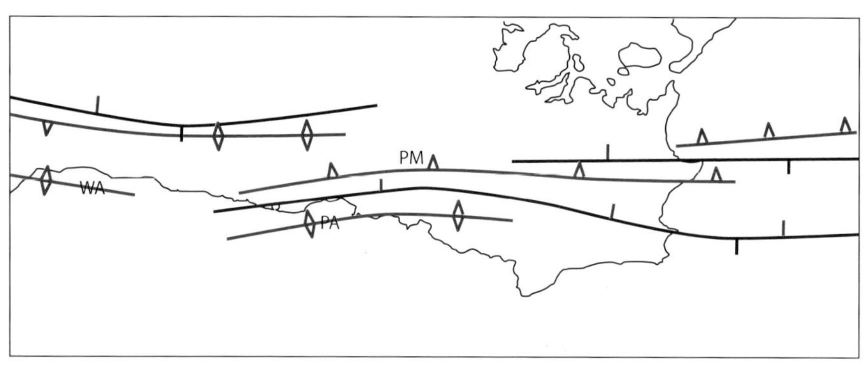

B. Main structural features of the area, redrawn from *A Seismic Atlas of Southern Britain*, BGS, 2005.

WA = Weymouth Anticline; PA = Purbeck Anticline; PM = Purbeck Monocline.

Black lines are faults. Black and red ticks show the direction of down-throw: black Jurassic/Cretaceous caused by stretching, and red Cenozoic caused by squeezing.

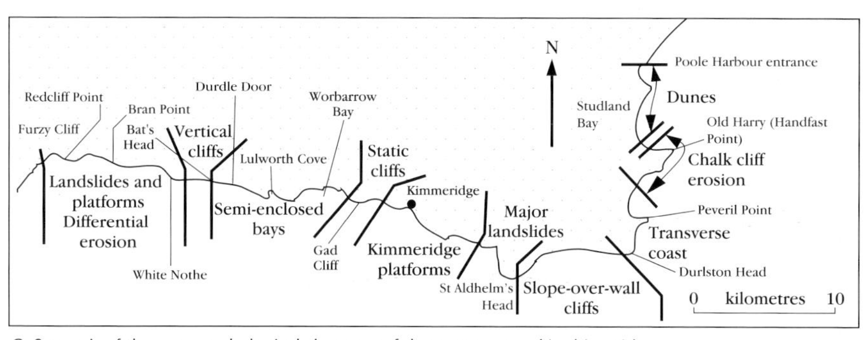

C. Synopsis of the geomorphological character of the coast covered in this guide.

The attitude of strata significantly affects the evolution and structure of cliffs.

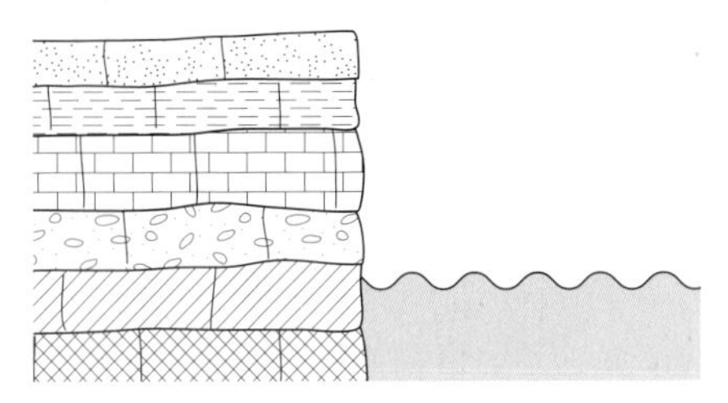

A. Horizontal at sea level.

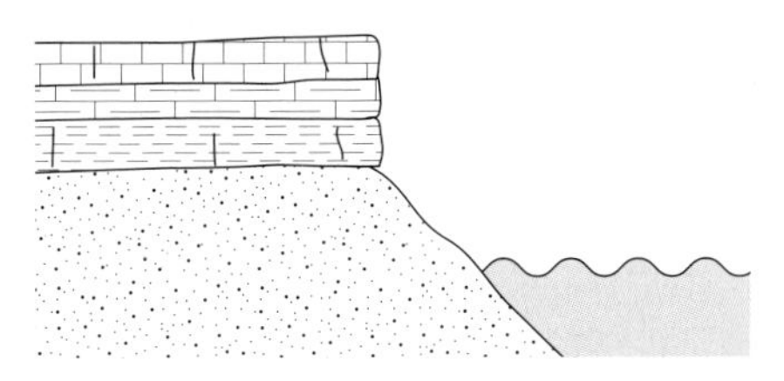

B. Horizontal capping cliffs.

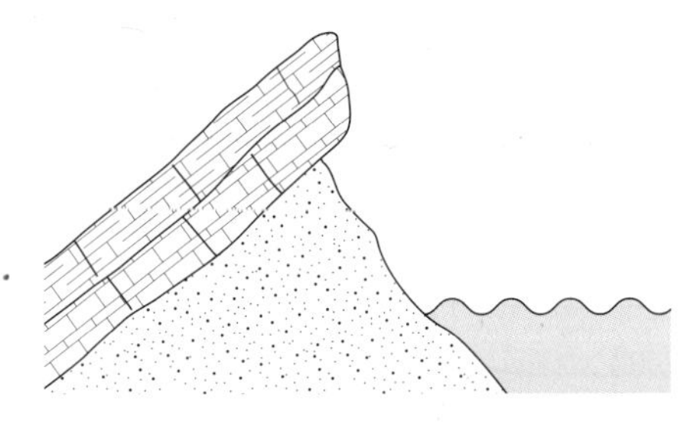

C. Steeply inclined.

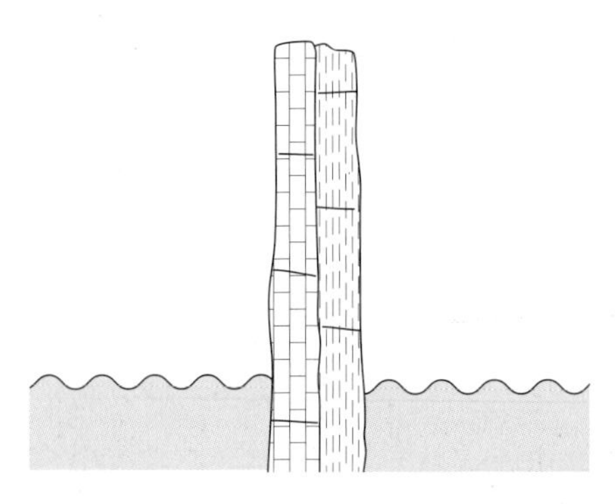

D. Near vertical.

Swyre Head – vertical white Chalk Subgroup
Bat's Head – vertical Chalk
Weymouth lowlands within the Weymouth Anticline
Scratchy Bottom – a dry valley partially filled with solifluction deposits
Bat's Hole – a natural arch
Low angle (thrust) fault plane with caves eroded by the sea (see inset)

During the 1980s researchers pointed out that there were both dry valleys and others occupied by streams inland from Lulworth Cove and Worbarrow Bay, but none into Stair Hole. They suggested that during a period when the sea level was lower, streams would have cut down through the Portland Stone barrier, a very different process from that forming Stair Hole. The stream combined with low-sea-level theory has been put to the test using side-scan sonar. This shows that the reefs and rock ledges present outside Lulworth Cove have not been cut through by a stream. The possibility that the stream cut down to present-day sea level without cutting down through the Portland strata offshore remains an option.

Another suggestion is that a north–south fault provided the line of weakness which the sea exploited: the side-scan sonar has shown evidence of minor faulting south of the cove's entrance.

There is consensus that a rising sea level coupled with the slow sinking of southern Britain, triggered by the decay of the great ice sheets at the end of the last glaciation, around 14,000 years ago, would have seen the sea encroach on an already ancient landscape. Current thinking suggests one or more phases of cove formation and enlargement while sea levels were higher than those seen today, doubtless following

Stair Hole viewed from the east. Particularly apparent are the complex relationships of strata of the Purbeck Limestone Group, which, as they have been tilted, have detached and slipped down dip under gravity, becoming increasingly disorganised.

the line of the stream which itself may well have been developing the weak line provided by the fault.

The bays and coves become increasingly large from Durdle Door beach eastwards as the thickness of strata between the Portland Stone Formation and the Chalk which forms the back walls increases and the dip decreases.

Landslides are an active reminder that the processes that have produced the

Chalk stacks at Handfast Point, known as Old Harry (the tallest one) and his wife. The Chalk is horizontally bedded and distinctive bands of flint nodules are present.

Lulworth Cove viewed from the south-east. How the Portland Stone Member was breached remains contentious, with both an ancestral stream to the one which flows into the cove today and evidence of faulting on the sea floor outside the cove's entrance both figuring in the debate.

beautiful Isle of Purbeck coast are ongoing and often very dramatic. There are examples of ancient landslides at White Nothe (pp. 48–9) and St Aldhelm's Head (pp. 78–80), and more recent ones have occurred between Mupe Bay and Arish Mell (p. 67), below Flower's Barrow (pp. 56–7) and at Ballard Down (p. 98). Evidence of old landslides are the boulder arcs seen on the shore and out beyond low-water mark. Many are of some antiquity and connected to the fluctuations in temperature and sea level seen during the last 2.65 million years of the Pleistocene and Holocene.

Lulworth Cove viewed from east to west at sea level.

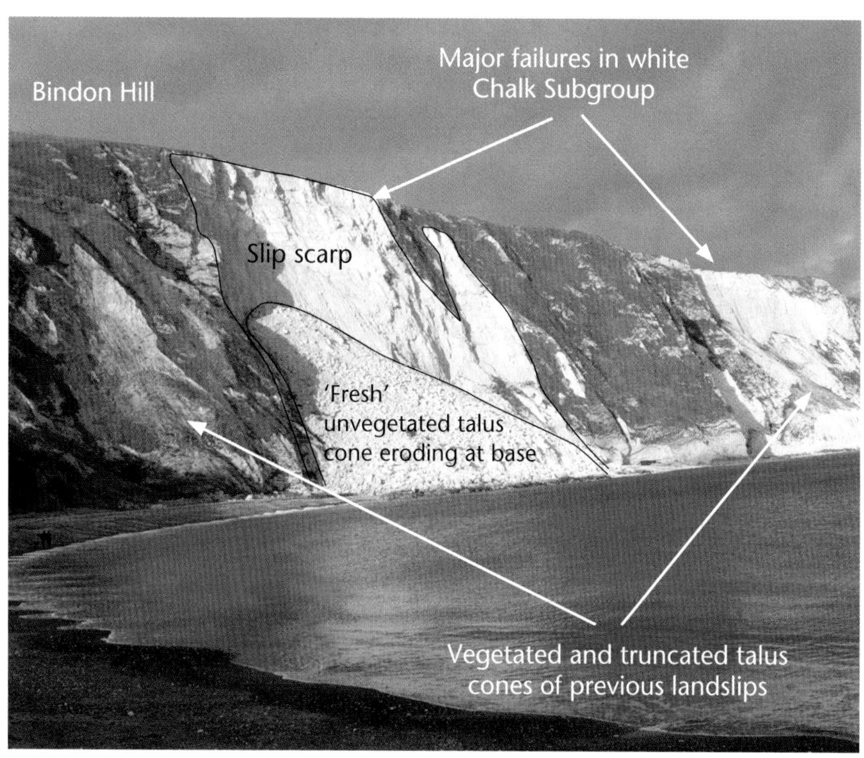

Major rock slides affecting the cliffs on the seaward side of Bindon Hill, viewed from Mupe Bay. The degree of vegetation growing over both fractured surface and talus cones provides clues as to the relative ages of these failures. The toes of the cones are being eroded back by the sea.

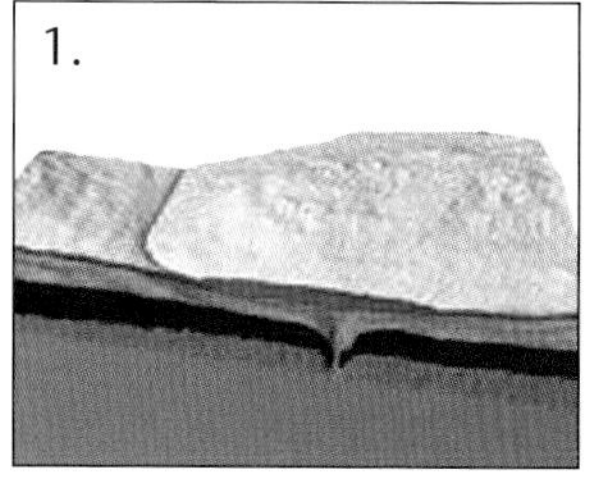

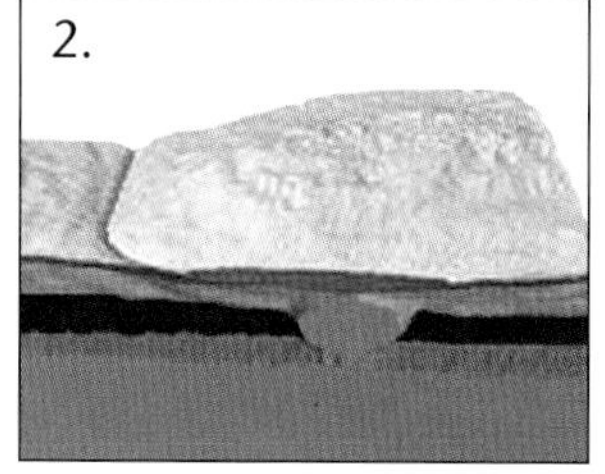

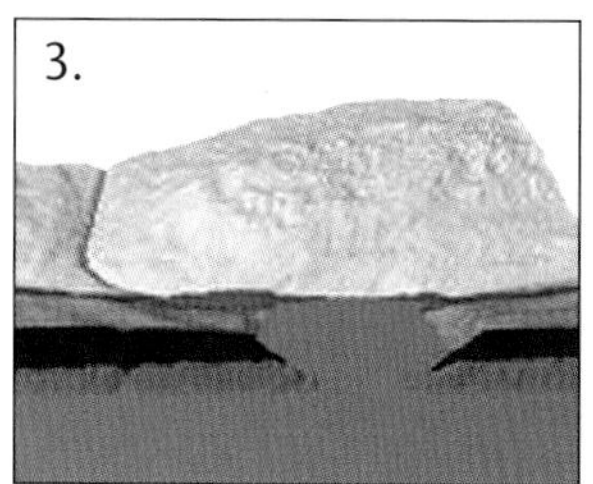

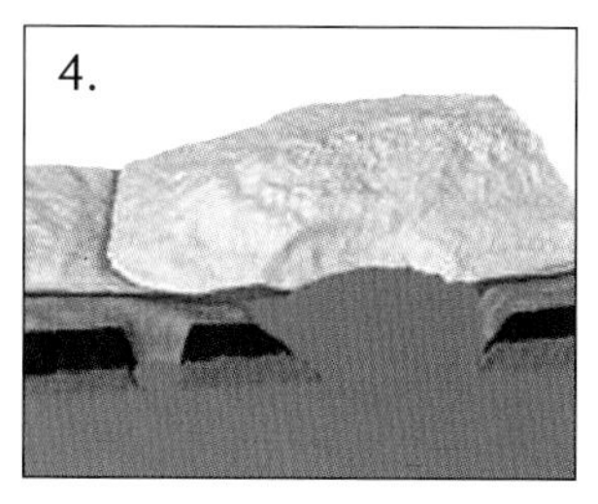

The stream theory for the evolution of Lulworth Cove has a watercourse breaching the barrier during a period of low sea level. Rising sea level sees the narrow breach widened, softer strata behind being eroded and Lulworth Cove forming over thousands of years. However, sea-floor mapping has revealed no evidence of a stream cutting down through the strata outside the cove or at its entrance. Perhaps the stream cut a notch much higher up and high sea levels developed that breach.

Worbarrow Tout to Chapman's Pool

The beaches can be accessed from Kimmeridge Bay, where there is ample car parking, and Chapman's Pool, where the nearest car park is at Worth Matravers. The narrow strip of beach between the two should only be accessed at low water or on a falling tide: it is very easy to be cut off by the rising tide. There is a splendid Visitor Centre at Kimmeridge with information on the geology and marine life.

Highlights include dramatic jagged cliffs, a nodding donkey, fossil ammonites, dolomite bands, Kimmeridge coal, and dark, eroding shale cliffs.

N.B. The section as far as Broad Bench, just west of Kimmeridge Bay, is a continuation of the restricted access area imposed by the MoD, first encountered immediately east of Lulworth Cove (p. 51).

The section between Worbarrow Tout and Chapman's Pool is dominated by the Portland Group and Kimmeridge Clay Formation. Parts of this section are virtually inaccessible and best viewed from the sea (see p. 105). Immediately beyond Worbarrow Tout is the small embayment of Pondfield Cove, where, once again, parts of the lower Purbeck Limestone Group are exposed. Here the concrete 'dragon's teeth' of one of the Second World War's defensive lines provide a faint echo of the jagged tilted strata! From here, Gad Cliff rises dramatically to the east, capped by the basal beds of the Purbeck Limestone Group, but the main buttress

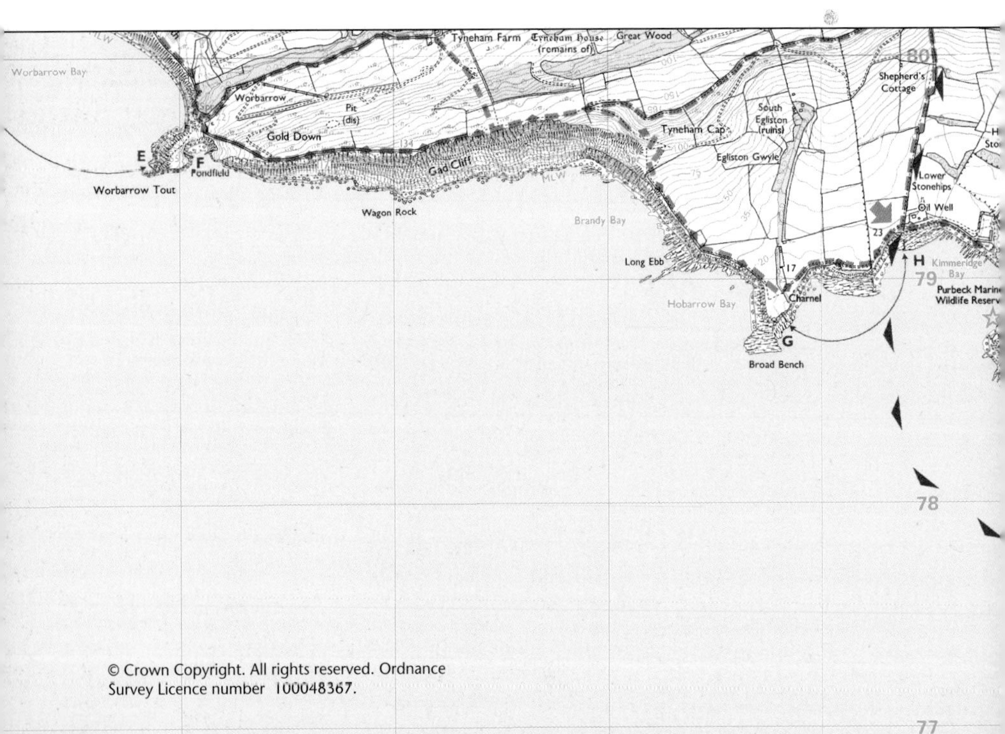

Worbarrow Tout with Gad Cliff rearing up beyond. The stability of these cliffs is greatly aided by their steep northerly dip, precarious-looking blocks being held in place until they are sufficiently undermined to suffer catastrophic failure.

is of the imposing Portland Stone Formation, tilted slightly west of north at around 50 degrees. A consequence of this is that as you proceed slightly south of east, you see progressively older strata in the lower part of the cliff, though mostly cloaked by fallen debris from above and slumped material from the softer Kimmeridge Clay Formation. The latter becomes increasingly evident, forming the cliffs of Brandy Bay, while the Portland Group sediments continue inland and, together with a veneer of Purbeck sediments, cap the hills that encompass the cliff-top plateau on which nestle the village of Kimmeridge, and Smedmore and Encombe houses. Portland Group sediments return to the coast crowning the summits of Houns-tout, round to St Aldhelm's Head (p. 77) and then on to Durlston Head.

Though this section has been described as '... an unattractive ... trackless wilderness abounding in adders', the grandeur of Gad Cliff is unforgettable. The east flank of Pondfield Cove immediately demonstrates the way in which joints and bedding planes control the form of the cliff, an aspect emphasised by the angularity of the surface of the cliff, which rises to around 130m above sea level. The strata dipping inland counterbalance the gravitational pull on the exposed blocks. This is eventually overcome when retreat at the foot undercuts and destabilises the great crags. The result is the tidal zone and lower cliff strewn with blocks, some as big as a small house, which have dropped, some recently, as evidenced by

The cliff just beyond Pondfield Cove, at the foot of Gad Cliff. The bedding planes and joints (three directions indicated) control the development of the cliff.

The lower part of the Portland Stone Formation is know as the Portland Chert Member. Fallen blocks exhibit what appear to be burrow systems that have been filled with chert.

the freshly broken rock surfaces. They are frequently full of chert, which appears to have formed within the back-filled branching burrows of crustaceans. At the eastern end, the lower slope of the cliff is the Kimmeridge Clay, overlain by the Portland Sand Formation, with a well-developed notch close to the top of the latter formation. Above this is the Portland Chert Member, towards the top of which is a bed of limestone cut by distinctive chert bands at an angle of about 45 degrees. Above is the Portland Freestone Member, which, at Swanworth Quarry (NGR SY 967783) and east from St Aldhelm's Head has been quarried and mined for crushed aggregate and dimension stone.

As the outcrop of the Portland Group strata recedes inland and the foot of the cliff is no longer afforded the protection of the blocks fallen from the heights, the blue-grey to black Kimmeridge Clay Formation begins to appear in sea-scoured, near-vertical and constantly crumbling cliffs. These stretch virtually uninterrupted as far as Houns-tout, where once again the protective spread of fallen Portland Group strata lead to an altogether gentler and less well-exposed slope (see above). The naming of this formation is down to the excellent exposure of a large part of the succession in and around Kimmeridge Bay, where the strata form a gentle anticlinal or

A nodding donkey above Kimmeridge Bay has become a familiar part of the landscape since the first one was installed in the 1950s.

domed structure. The anticline encouraged BP to drill for oil in the 1950s – and oil they found. The reservoir appeared to be relatively small and although predicted to produce for only a short time, over 50 years on, oil still flows. Though many theories have been proposed for this longevity, including the reservoir being fed from another source, production figures show that there has been a real decline in daily production and this supports a finite oil reserve from the predicted anticlinal trap that has turned out to be larger than previously thought. The lower part of the succession is exposed further to the west.

Despite a great deal of research, our understanding of the Kimmeridge Clay Formation and the conditions under which the sediments accumulated is still challenged: the evidence gleaned does not always square up. The strata exposed in the cliffs are composed of a number of different sediment types. Mudstones, with more or less carbonate present, predominate: little or no bedding is preserved. The shales invariably contain more organic matter. Sometimes this is high enough to form oil shales that are black-brown in colour and have a waxy feel. Unlike the mudstones, the shales are not bioturbated and readily split into thin laminae. They are the product of an oxygen-starved sea floor where organic-rich detritus accumulated, and where no living animals churned the sediment. In stark contrast to the blue-grey to black mudrocks, starkly white, fine-grained limestone bands are also occasionally present. These coccolith-rich sediments formed as a result of blooms rather like those we periodically witness in modern oceans. Researchers have recognised patterns in the succession of these different packages of sediment, describing them as cycles or rhythms. These have been ascribed by some to astronomical cycles.

Also present within the Kimmeridge Clay are 14 distinct yellow-brown weathering dolomites. The formation of these was triggered by the changing chemistry of the sediments during burial under a thick pile of sediment. One of these bands shows strange polygonal dish-shaped structures with small thrusts, which have been explained as expansion structures – though questions have been asked as to why similar structures are not present in the other 13 stone bands. These stone bands form the ledges within Kimmeridge Bay and along the coast, and have found use as a local building stone. Disruption of the well-defined and gently sloping beds permits the identification of the not infrequent 'north–south' faults present along this section.

The Flats Stone Band in Kimmeridge Bay. The name is ironic, as this bed is anything but flat, being characterised by polygonal dish-shaped structures and small-scale thrusts which appear to have resulted from the chemical alteration and consequent expansion of the stone band while buried.

A variety of sedimentary structures within individual beds have been identified and have fascinating stories to tell. Examples include deposits of broken fragments of partially solidified sediment: these have been linked to severe storms. Tiny fractures with a similar orientation and filled with sediment from an overlying bed may be the result of earthquakes which caused mini-ruptures on the sea floor, sucking sediment into the cracks.

The wealth of fossil evidence representing life and death in the sea, in the air and on land continues to astonish; the discovery, preparation and care of such material require great dedication and skill (p. 75). Shelly plasters along bedding planes in the organic-rich shales tell of brief interludes estimated at no more than six years when colonisation of the sea floor became possible. Ammonites are frequently seen as flattened impressions on bedding planes. Males and females, known as microconchs

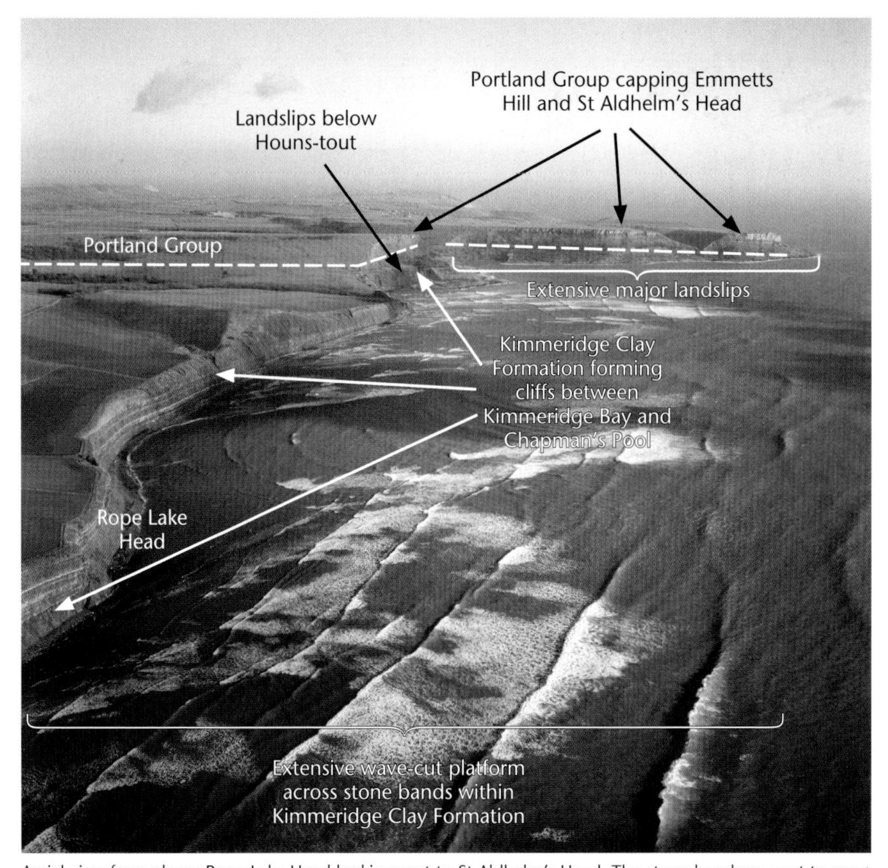

Aerial view from above Rope Lake Head looking east to St Aldhelm's Head. The stone bands run out to sea forming great sweeping ledges over which the sea breaks, providing habitat for a rich flora and fauna, and an open laboratory to study the complex structures within the Kimmeridge Clay Formation.

and macroconchs respectively, have been recognised and rare ammonite eggs discovered and described. A wealth of other invertebrates has been found, including barnacles and tiny brittle-stars. The most spectacular remains are the vertebrates: sharks, rays and many other bony fishes, marine reptiles including crocodiles, and the pliosaurs with jaws over 2m long. The damage that could be inflicted by these rulers of the sea is sometimes seen on the bones of other marine reptiles, where a series of deep puncture marks pays dramatic testimony to the life and death struggles in this sea. The delicate wing bones and jaws of pterosaurs have been recovered and even the occasional terrestrial giant has found a final resting place in these sediments. The limbs of giant sauropods have been found along with the partial skeletons of the meat eaters of the day.

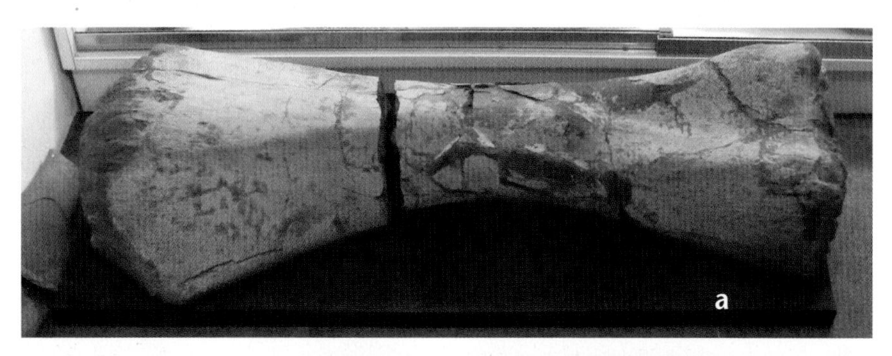

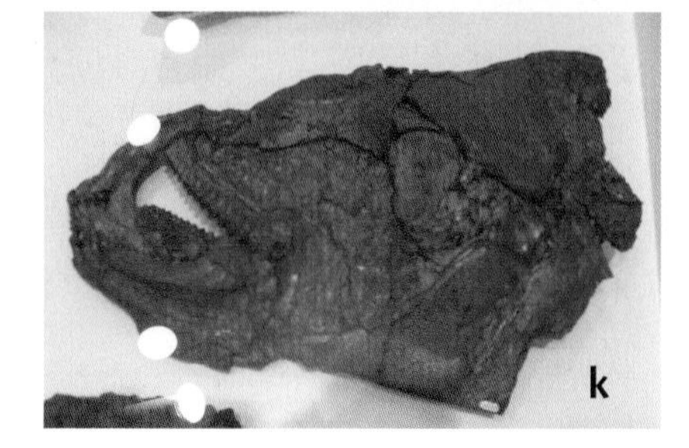

Fossils collected and prepared by Steve Etches.

- **a** Humerus of a sauropod (dinosaur)
- **b–i** Ammonites
- **b–c** *Pectinatites* macroconchs (females)
- **d–f** *Pectinatites* microconchs (male)
- **g–i** *Gravesia* (ammonites)
- **j** *Rhinobatos* (ray) and other fish remains
- **k** Skull of *Gyrodus* (fish)

Collections

The coming together of fossil-rich strata and curious minds has triggered the collection of fossils since the earliest times. Prehistoric burials have been excavated in which echinoids and necklaces made of perforated spherical sponges from the Chalk were found. The change of mindset from 'curious' to 'enquiring' is crucial to the development of any science, and palaeontology has been no exception. Underpinning that change were the increasingly important collections of fossils built up by the educated and often leisured classes during the eighteenth and nineteenth centuries. From the gentleman's 'Cabinet' and the rapidly developing network of museums, which housed both individual finds and cabinet collections no longer tolerated within a home, the classification of life-past would begin. Dorset has played a major part in the advancement of palaeontology, and fossils from the county, especially the coast, are to be found in many major collections both in the UK and around the world.

There are a number of important collections of fossils housed locally. Steve Etches's internationally important collection of superb and exquisitely prepared invertebrates and vertebrates from the Kimmeridge Clay Formation is housed in Kimmeridge. This is a collection fuelling new research. Plans to house this collection in a purpose-built museum with public access in Kimmeridge are at an advanced stage. At Worth Matravers, the Square and Compass pub has a small but fine and changing collection of local (Kimmeridge Clay to Chalk) fossils and

Steve Etches (left) showing visitors his extraordinary collection of Kimmeridge Clay Formation fossils.

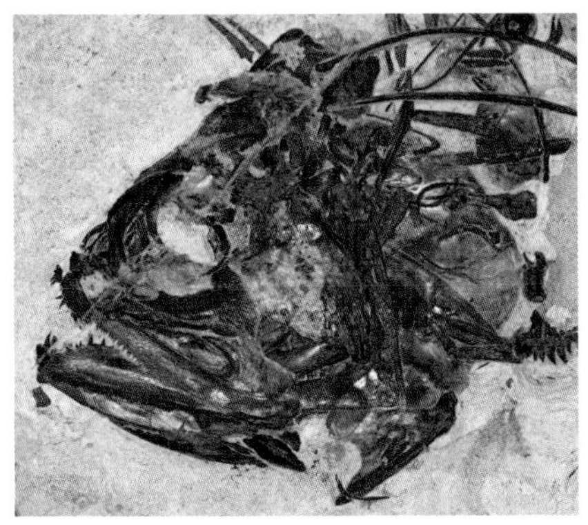

Skull of *Thrissops* (fish).

Ammonite showing evidence of predation; the bite mark is located by the letter b.

Fossils collected and prepared by Steve Etches.

more recent antiquities in the custodianship of Charlie Newman. Happily, opening times are synchronised with opening times! The Dorset County Museum in Dorchester has a Jurassic Coast Gallery which displays specimens from this stretch of coast.

The Dorset County Museum, founded in 1846, has a fine collection of geological specimens which represents the whole of the Jurassic Coast, and the work of many amateur and professional geologists over 160 years.

The Square and Compass boasts a fascinating collection of local fossils – and other finds – started by Raymond Newman and continued by his son Charlie, the landlord, and daughter Mary.

Commercial interest in the Kimmeridge Clay extends back a long time. Examples of worked oil shale have been found in excavated prehistoric and Roman sites. Probably these peoples were aware that the oil shale could be burned – hence the name 'Kimmeridge coal'. During the seventeenth century 'Kimmeridge coal' was a source of fuel for the production of alum, used in the dyeing industry, from the local shales, salt from sea water and in the production of glass. The nineteenth century saw a revival of interest, with the oil shale being quarried and mined from the cliffs, and exported by sea to other parts of the UK and France to be used for the production of oil, gas and other chemicals. A high sulphur content, all too apparent if an attempt is made to ignite a piece of this shale, was not a strong selling point, as the local inhabitants were very well aware. Spontaneous combustion of these shales has occurred (pp. 23–4).

Before following the cliffs eastward mention must be made of discoveries of much younger fossils in the area around Encombe and St Aldhelm's Head. Bones of some of the mammals which wandered across Dorset during the Pleistocene were found. They included rhinoceros, mammoth and auroch – the ancestor of our domesticated cattle.

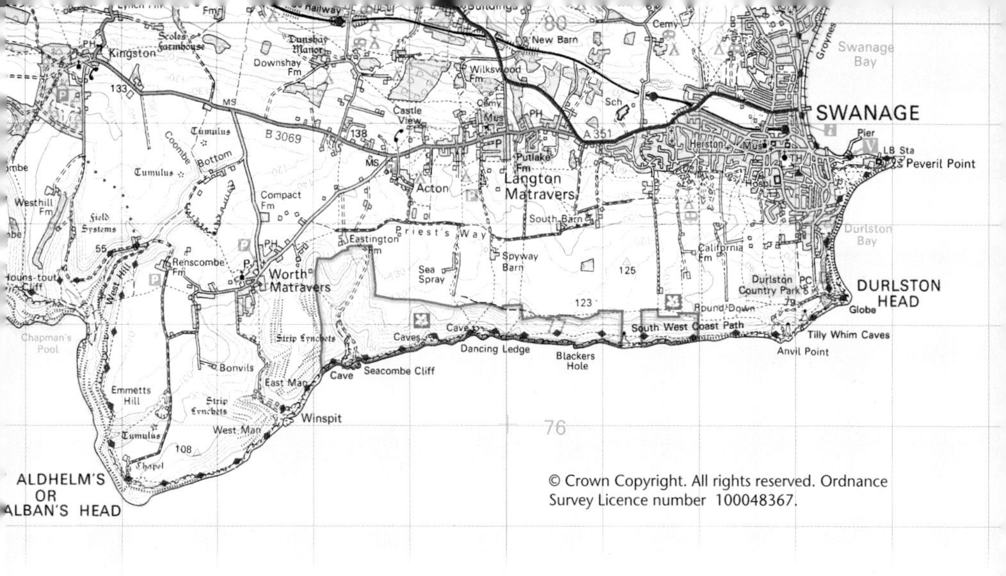

Chapman's Pool to Swanage

There are no beaches along this section but the water's edge can be accessed at the old quarry workings of Winspit, Seacombe and Dancing Ledge. Durlston Country Park has excellent visitor facilities and car parks.

This is a dramatic and remote section of coast where sheer cliffs plunge straight into the sea and where others are defended by occasional boulder fields fed by landslides. Highlights include wonderful views of the dramatic cliffs with nesting seabirds and wild orchids (in season), cliff quarries and rugged bays.

The Kimmeridge Clay Formation's last appearances are at Chapman's Pool and on the shore, just below the west side of St Aldhelm's Head. The small outcrops below St Aldhelm's Head are the most eastern of the Kimmeridge Formation on the south coast of England. The larger exposure was once famed for beautiful three-dimensional ammonites, unlike the flattened examples so familiar through much of the formation. Reputedly they could be found in abundance, washed out on the shore, though if true, that abundance is long gone. Doubtless those specimens graced many a mantelpiece and collector's cabinet alike.

To the east, the Portland Group forms the towering cliff summits of Emmetts Hill and St Aldhelm's Head, with great spreads of boulders and fallen debris littering a series of troughs and crests, like a frozen movie frame of a heavy sea. Landsliding is a significant process here, and cyclically, new falls feed the glacier-like flows below, heaving paths and tracks, and pushing the vegetated and boulder-strewn slips ever seawards. Some of the fallen rock debris below the cliffs at the head is the product of quarrying. When they reach sea level, the boulder spreads afford valuable protection, impeding the progress of marine erosion.

Back from the cliff top, a capping of the lower part of the Purbeck Limestone Group is present, sometimes appearing in the cliff section east towards Winspit. Access

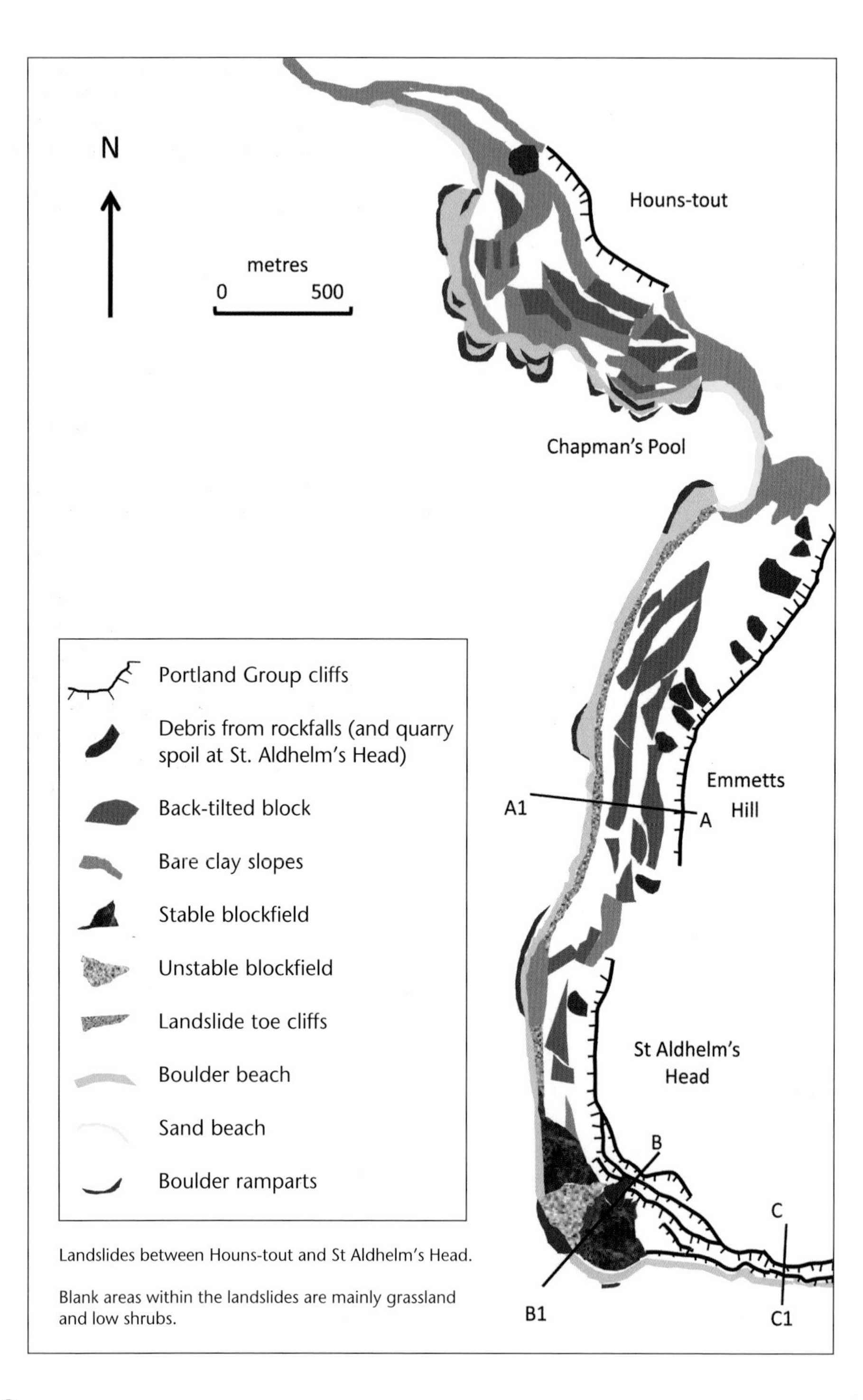

Landslides between Houns-tout and St Aldhelm's Head.

Blank areas within the landslides are mainly grassland and low shrubs.

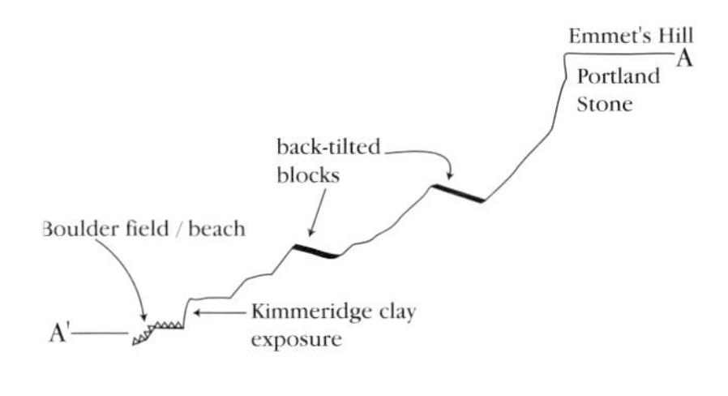

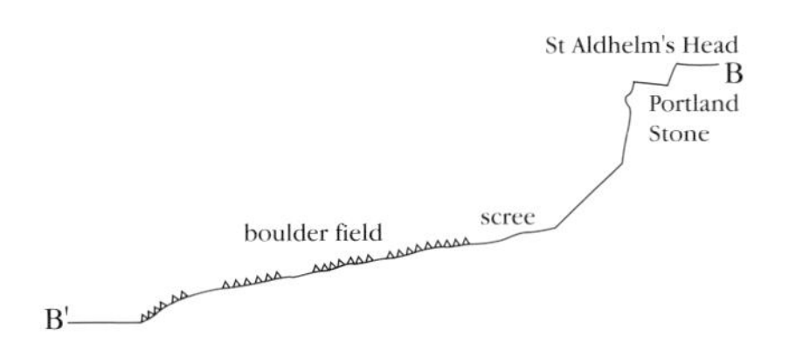

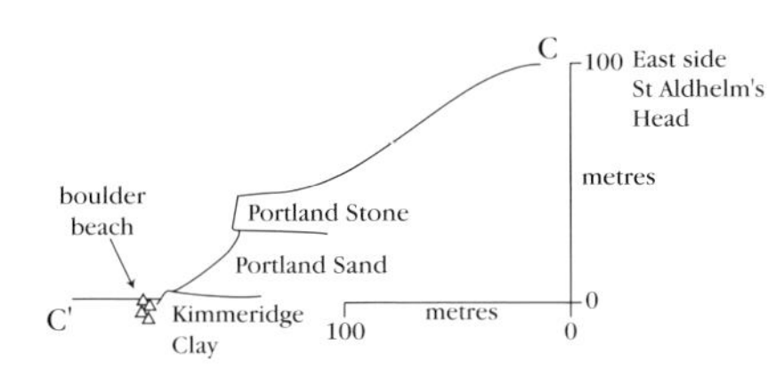

Profiles marked on figure opposite.

across the slips below these cliffs is far from easy and, like at Gad Cliff (p. 68), not without its hazards. The cliff-top path provides fine views along the coast, and occasionally allows access to the sea, as at Winspit, Seacombe and Dancing Ledge (p. 86). To appreciate these cliffs fully, advantage should be taken of the boat trips which run at certain times of the year (see p. 105).

The cliffs east from St Aldhelm's Head (108m) to Durlston Head are dominated by the Portland Group, which for the most part dips gently eastwards. The Portland Sand Formation is below sea level, though close to Dancing Ledge it is briefly brought to sea level by faults, one with a throw of 24m. The cliffs otherwise consist of the Portland Stone Formation, providing a formidable bulwark to the sea, and with intricate joints and bedding planes: a seabird heaven. Dramatic cliff falls do occur from time to time. The stone's value for building was recognised long ago, and the presence of such a sought-

The view along the Purbeck coast looking west towards St Aldhelm's Head is dominated by precipitous cliffs cut in the Portland Stone Group.

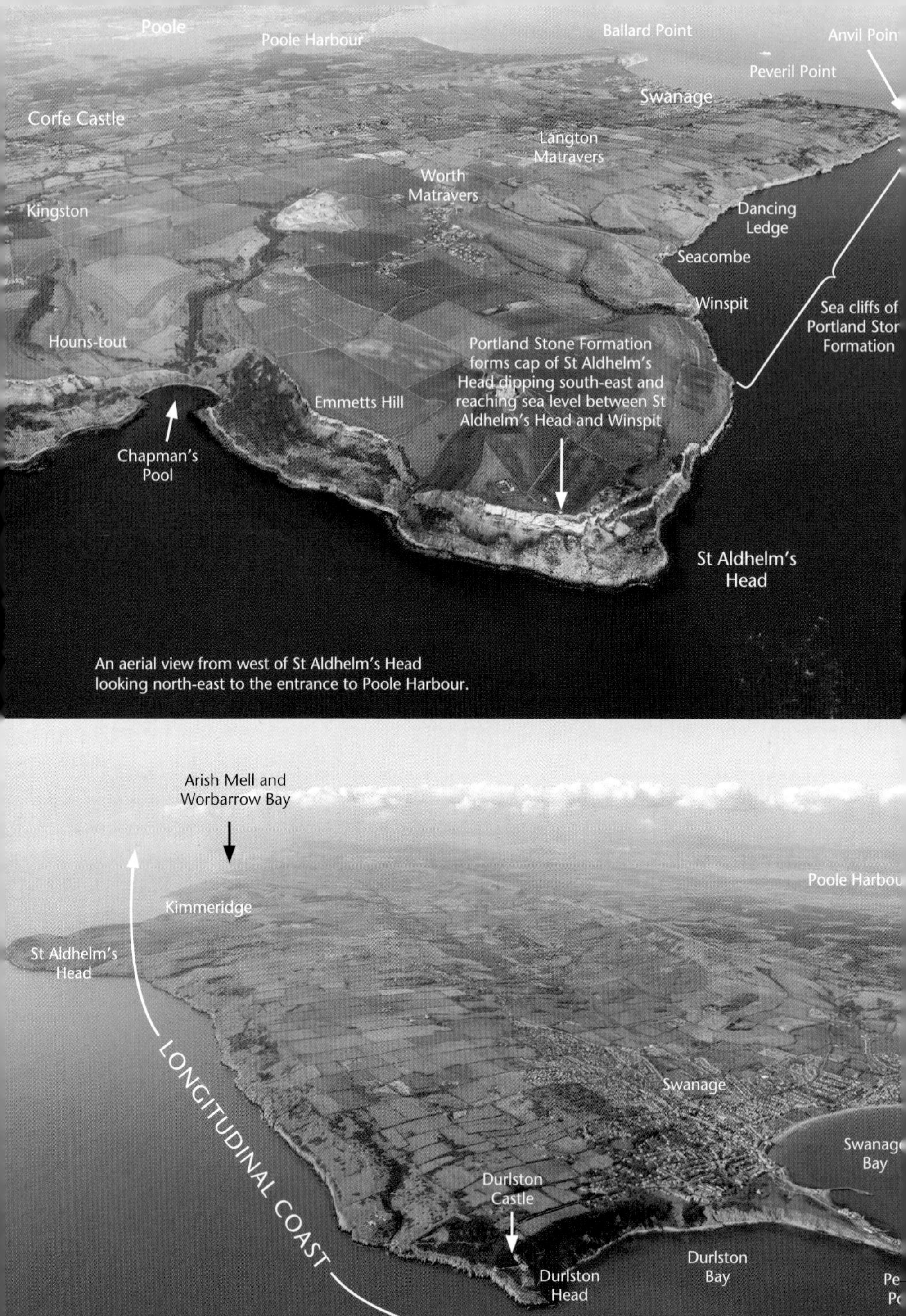

An aerial view from west of St Aldhelm's Head looking north-east to the entrance to Poole Harbour.

Durlston Head is the point where the geographer's longitudinal coast, followed from west to east, becomes a transverse coast running north to south.

These disused stone workings in the cliffs east of Winspit speak eloquently for the ingenuity of past generations of quarrymen. Following the sought-after 'cliff stone' (Portland Freestone Member), they have left pillars to support the roof of the gallery, and in one case the pillar has been undercut and waste stone stacked to support the remaining pillar and roof. The floor of the gallery is the top of the Portland Chert Member.

after resource so close to the means by which transport became possible, unsurprisingly led to the development of cliff quarries (pp. 85–6). Quarrymen's 'graffiti' picture the types of boat that were used.

Quarry 'graffiti': a picture of a boat, possibly of the type used to collect the stone, incised on the wall of one of the galleries at Tilly Whim Caves, presumably cut by a quarryman.

Like the cliffs of Kimmeridge Clay, the gently dipping strata provide an opportunity to detect the variations between beds, and using marker horizons, the eye is able to detect the sudden changes in their relative positions, denoting what in quarryman's parlance is a 'jump' or fault. The cliffs provide a record of these features, for once traced inland they become more difficult to see, obscured beneath the largely vegetated Purbeck plateau.

George Burt and Durlston Castle

George Burt 1816–94

George Burt, self-styled 'King of Swanage', spent his early years working in the Purbeck stone quarries above the town. When 19 years old he went to London to work for his uncle, John Mowlem, in the construction industry and develop his business skills. By the age of 40 he was a wealthy man, married with six children and wanting to return home. In 1857 he bought Purbeck House in Swanage High Street. Burt was perhaps a typical self-made man of the nineteenth Century, determined and enterprising. However, when he returned home he rather arrogantly tried to show the quarrymen and acquaintances of his youth how they ought to run their town and almost how

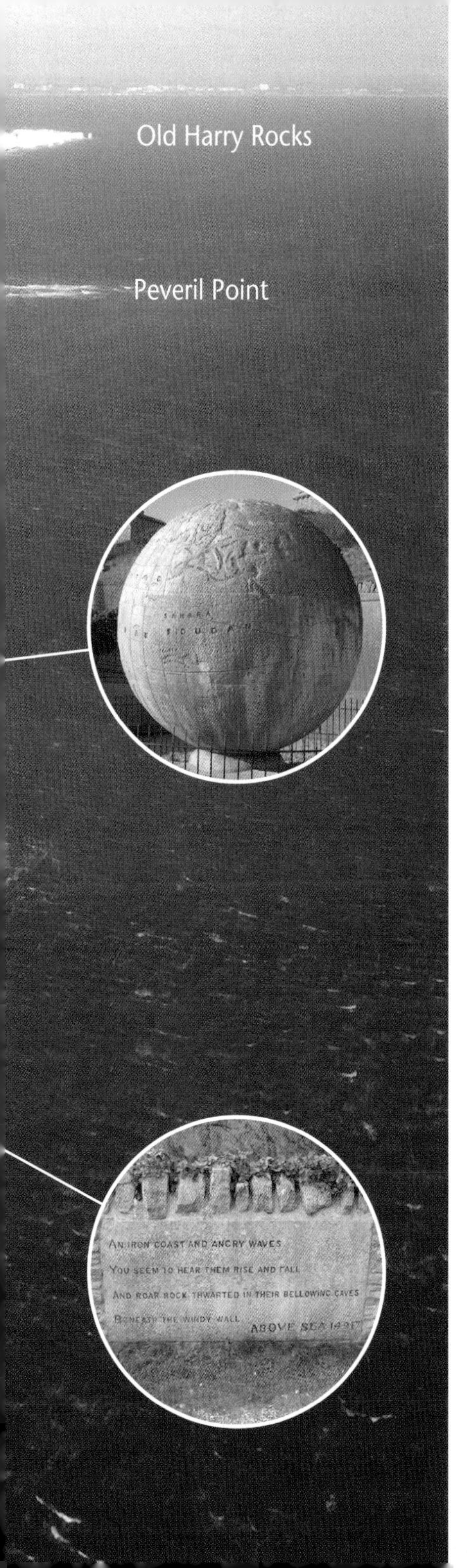

to run their lives. There was resentment about this, of course, but one development, a failure as it happens, has left a lasting legacy from which Swanage has undoubtedly benefited.

In 1862, Burt purchased the Cliff and Sentry Estate at Durlston, at the time semi-industrial and scarred by quarrying. Assisted by the architect George Crickmay, Burt drew up a plan for a major up-market residential development with new roads, well-laid-out gardens, paths, seats, water supplies, gas mains and lamp posts, and Durlston Castle as the centrepiece. The development failed to attract buyers but the castle, Great Globe, many London artefacts and a multitude of carved inscriptions remain, such as those along the path near the castle and down to the main viewpoint.

Durlston Castle (built between 1887 and 1891) in the splendid Durlston Country Park, owned by Dorset County Council, is currently in the process of being restored and will eventually contain a plethora of information on the area's geology and wildlife. In addition, Burt's artefacts are being painstakingly repaired and new ones added. Though it was a failure as a housing development, Burt would probably have been pleased to see the estate develop the way it has.

Thomas Hardy visited Swanage in the 1870s and he and his wife Emma regularly walked the cliffs and shore. In his diary he notes:

'Evening. Just after sunset. Sitting with E. on a stone under the wall ... the sounds are two, and only two. On the left, Durlston Head roaring high and low, like a giant asleep. On the right a thrush. Above the bird hangs the new moon and a steady planet.'

GROUP	FORMATION	Strahan (1898)	Arkell (1947)	Other names
PORTLAND GROUP (part)	PORTLAND STONE FORMATION	Shrimp Stone	Shrimp Bed	
		Blue Stone	Titanites Bed	Spangle
		Top, Upper or Pond Freestone	Pond Freestone	
		Flint Stone	Chert Vein	Flint Vein
		Nist Bed	House Cap	The Listy Bed
		House Cap		Spangle
		Under picking Cap	Under picking Cap	
		Under Freestone	Under Freestone	Bottom Freestone
		Cliff Beds	Cherty Series	Includes 'Sea Ledges' and 'Prickle Bed' or 'Puffin Ledge'.

Table showing the names applied to strata of the Portland Stone Formation on the Isle of Purbeck by Strahan (1898) and Arkell (1947).

These cliffs, the old quarries and the galleries driven into them (see p. 81) provide unrivalled opportunities, where accessible and safe, to view the various beds of stone to which the quarrymen gave singular names. The Chert-bearing beds are the 'Cliff Beds' within which is the 'Prickle Bed' or 'Puffin Ledge', so named as a ledge is formed where the softer sediments are weathered out, and the resulting groove is used by puffins. Sandwiched between the 'Cliff Beds' and the 'Underpicking Cap' with overlying 'House Cap' – also known as 'Spangle' (but see below) – is the 'Under Freestone', previously worked for staddle stones, kerbs and sinks. Initially this was worked back from the cliff, but as the overburden became greater, it was followed underground, where pillar and stall working was employed. Stone was removed, while regularly spaced pillars of unworked stone were left to support the roof, or supports were made of stacks of unwanted stone. The moulds and casts of ammonites with the name *Titanites*, on account of their very large size, are not uncommon in these strata and are sometimes seen in the ceilings of the mines (see p. 104). The 'Listy Bed', 'Flint Vein', and the 'Upper Freestone' also known as the 'Pond Freestone', follow. Next is the 'Blue Stone' or 'Spangle' – this time the real Spangle! The name derives from the sparkling calcite crystals which fill cavities in the stone. This bed is also especially rich in the ammonite *Titanites anguiformis*, which can attain a diameter of nearly a metre. Finally there is the 'Shrimp Bed', so named as crustaceans are present. This horizon has yielded a halite pseudomorph or 'fossil' salt crystal, hinting at the changing environments and heralding the Purbeck Limestone Group sediments. Tilly Whim Caves, named after the type of crane used to lower blocks of stone to waiting boats between Anvil Point and Durlston Head, are a further example of concentrated quarrying and mining activity. Long disused and once open to the public, safety concerns led to their closure in the 1970s. At this location, the 'Spangle' is replaced by an oyster patch-reef.

Quarrs and Quarries

Quarrying within the Isle of Purbeck continues as an important local industry. Before mechanisation, quarrying was at the core of several local communities. Portland and Purbeck stone was quarried and mined in 'undergrounds' for buildings and monuments. Clays were dug for making bricks and tiles, while limestone, including the Chalk, was burned in kilns for the production of lime used in building and for agriculture. Export of stone products is known during Roman times.

During the medieval period, Purbeck Marble became very fashionable for ledger slabs and decorative shafts in many of the great ecclesiastical buildings in England. Today, this sought-after stone is in demand for restoration work but also finds uses in high-quality ornamental work, testing the skills of the modern marbler. The Purbeck Marblers still hold an annual meeting, with appropriate archaic ritual, in Corfe Castle Town Hall.

A coloured engraving showing quarrying east of Anvil Point at Tilly Whim Caves.

The cliffs east and west of Seacombe bear witness to the quarrying industry which thrived for centuries along this coast.

The coastal outcrop provided relatively easy access to the Portland and Purbeck stone, even from the shore. Before the advent of modern road transport, the sea offered an immediate if somewhat hazardous way out. Quarries inevitably clustered near cliffs. Along the coast, there is evidence of this former industry. The clues may be subtle – wedge holes laboriously cut to free the block, a drill hole for an explosive charge which when fired left a distinctive shatter mark on the rock surface, an abandoned piece of dressed stone, quarryman's graffiti. Today's mind struggles to comprehend the skills required to load the substantial pieces of dressed stone on to frail wooden boats moored perilously close to cliffs.

Ceiling collapse and the stacked stone supports.

As the easily quarried Purbeck strata at the surface were depleted, so the same beds were chased down underground. The 'undergrounds' could cover considerable areas, so in today's mechanised world, where quarries reach depths unheard of in the past, the disused and forgotten galleries are sometimes encountered. An entrance to an underground is preserved in Durlston Country Park. The cliff-based industry burgeoned during the eighteenth and nineteenth centuries, gradually declining in the twentieth. The advent of mechanised road transport ended the sea-borne trade.

A beautiful corbelled arch and standing water in gallery.

The surface of a limestone within the Portland Chert Member at Dancing Ledge reveals worn ammonites and the parallel grooves down which either sledges or wheeled carts were run with stone for loading on to boats.

The entrance to an underground in Durlston Country Park, where Purbeck limestone was worked in numerous quarries and quarrs (underground workings) in the eighteenth and nineteenth centuries. In this underground, a limestone bed known as the 'New Vein' was extracted.

Durlston Head. The Portland and Purbeck strata are cut by a number of faults. These are especially significant north of the head, where the Portland Group is juxtaposed against the Purbeck Limestone Group. Very complex structures are produced in the lowest of the Purbeck strata.

Durlston Bay looking south towards Durston Head. In the middle distance is the coastal protection scheme carried out in the 1980s to protect properties built close to a fault zone on top of the cliff. The white lines mark the approximate position of the Cinder Member, an oyster-rich limestone, demonstrating the displacement caused by the faults (black lines).

The coast turns abruptly from an east–west (a geographer's longitudinal coast) to a north–south (a transverse coast) orientation at Durlston Head (p. 79), which also marks a more-or-less simultaneous and dramatic change from Portland to Purbeck sediments. This change is brought about by an east–west-trending fault, setting the latter against the former. Durlston Bay presents a magnificent section through the Purbeck Limestone Group, named after the Isle of Purbeck, dipping gently in a northerly direction. Faulting is responsible for the succession being largely repeated north of an east-north-east to west-south-west fault at the Zig-Zag path, which descends to the shore, about half-way around Durlston Bay. Just north of the Zig-Zag path, a great spread of rock is held in place and protected by rock-filled gabions

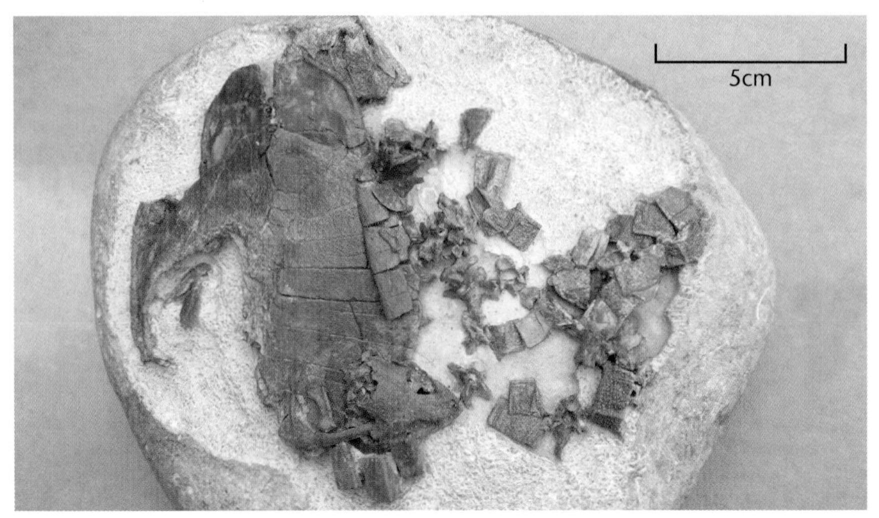

The fossilised remains of a small turtle including its skull, closely associated with the partial remains of a crocodile. The small boulder, with a few clues of what might lie within, was spotted by an eagle-eyed collector on a local beach. Many hours of painstaking preparation later and these stunning remains have been exposed.

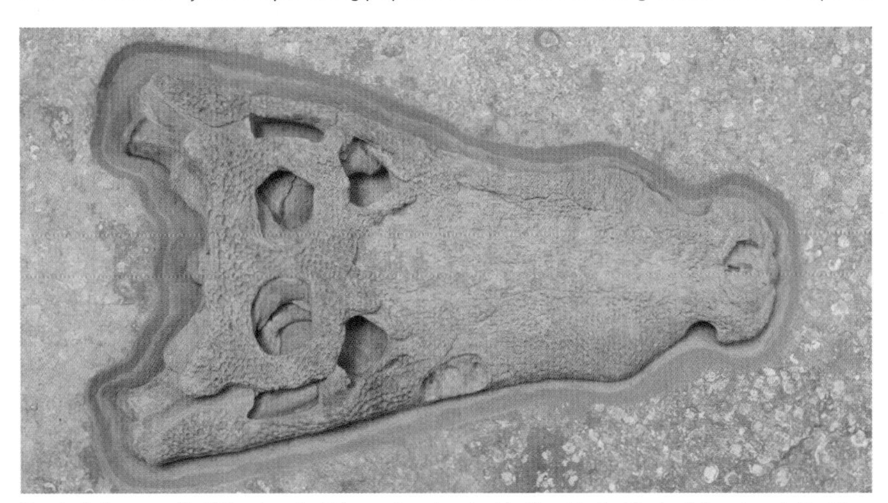

The skull of a crocodile (56cm long) which was found embedded in a block of Purbeck limestone in Durlston Bay. Many hours of careful preparation were required to expose the intricate detail of this fabulous specimen.

at the toe. This was constructed during the early 1980s to stop the cliff erosion, which threatened the flats built on the cliff top. The strata in Durlston Bay have been observed and collected from for over 160 years. During that time remarkable discoveries have been made, including celestine and calciostrontianite in the lower part of the succession. The presence of the former mineral confirmed that evaporites had been deposited. The strata are especially famous for the vertebrate remains which have been found, and finds made by Victorian collectors are of considerable historical and scientific importance.

Victorian Geologists

The Dorset coast was a magnet for many eminent Victorian geologists at a time when the science of geology had become established. Among them were Professor Edward Forbes and Henry W. Bristow of the recently created Geological Survey of England and Wales. They recorded sections and published these along with maps. In 1898 the first *Geological Survey Memoir* to include this coast, written by A. Strahan, was published.

Sir Richard Owen (1804–92), anatomist, first Superintendent of the British Museum (Natural History) in South Kensington, confidant of royalty and politicians, and author of many papers describing the fossil vertebrate remains found along the Dorset coast in the nineteenth century. In 1871 Owen described the mammals which Beckles had discovered in his excavation in a monograph of the Palaeontographical Society.

Discoveries of terrestrial vertebrates were made by the Swanage-based collectors William R. Brodie (b. *c.*1830) and Charles Willcox (b. 1809). These finds led Professor (later Sir) Richard Owen to encourage Samuel Husbands Beckles (1814–90), who had retired to the UK from the West Indies on health grounds, to prospect for the remains of tiny mammals in the Purbeck strata of Durlston Bay. His success in this venture was rewarded with additional support from Sir Charles Lyell and Charles Darwin. The Revd Peter

The illustration, based on a photograph by F. Briggs which accompanied Charles Kingsley's article 'Geological discoveries at Swanage', shows the excavations in Durlston Bay which Beckles funded in 1857. Beckles may be the formally dressed gentleman in the foreground.

Samuel Husbands Beckles (1814–90). Encouragement from Richard Owen, and his philanthropy, led to the recovery of a substantial collection of early Cretaceous mammals from an excavation in Durlston Bay.

The Reverend Osmond Fisher (1817–1914) documented Purbeck strata in Dorset, including those in Durlston Bay.

John Clavell Mansel-Pleydell (1817–1902) was a great amateur naturalist. During his life he collected many specimens which found their way into museum collections.

Bellinger Brodie (1815–97) made a remarkable collection of fossil insects, blazing a trail still being followed very actively in the twenty-first century. The Revds J.A. Austen (publishing during the 1850s) and Osmond Fisher (born at Osmington 1817, d. 1914) both produced sections of the strata in Durlston Bay. In 1881 the latter, who was not only a man of the cloth but also a geophysicist, became the second person to suggest a theory of plate tectonics – receiving similar scorn for his efforts. J.C. Mansel-Pleydell (1817–1902), who was instrumental in founding the Dorset Natural History and Antiquarian Field Club, presented many fine specimens to museums, including that in Dorchester. Among these specimens were the immense jaw and a paddle of *Pliosaurus grandis*.

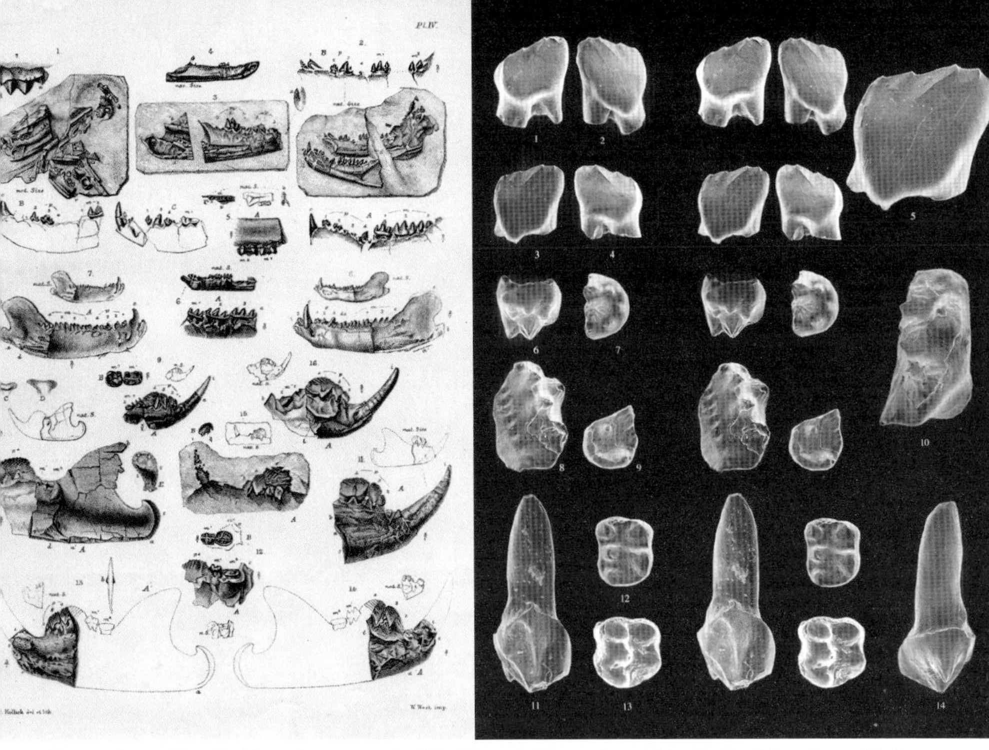

Then and now: Plate IV of Owen's monograph of the Mesozoic Mammals, published by the Palaeontographical Society in 1871, in which he described and figured the collection made by Samuel Beckles. The elaborate plate, engraved on metal, is in sharp contrast to the photographic plate of recently collected tiny teeth from similar mammals (multituberculates) to those seen in figures 9–16 of Owen's plate. These were photographed using a scanning electron microscope in the 1990s and are mostly stereo-pairs. The plate appeared as Plate 1 in Z. Kielan-Jaworowska, and P.C. Ensom, 'Multituberculate mammals from the Purbeck Limestone Formation (Upper Jurassic of southern England)', 1992, *Palaeontology*, **35**, 95–126, and is reproduced by kind permission of the Palaeontological Association.

The 2.04m long paddle of *Pliosaurus grandis*, a very large marine reptile from the Kimmeridge Clay Formation near Kimmeridge. The specimen was presented to the Dorset County Museum by J.C. Mansel-Pleydell.

The mandible of a small dinosaur, now known to have been a dromaeosaur, is one such example. This specimen had a rather chequered history, with identifications as both carnivorous lizard and crocodile. Perhaps more startlingly, there is a specimen of a small ichthyosaur collected in the nineteenth century. As the Purbeck sediments were essentially non-marine, this occurrence might have been regarded as unlikely. With that in mind, the specimen and surrounding matrix were 'forensically' examined, and the results have confirmed an origin in these strata. This work elegantly confirms the importance of museum collections where such specimens are preserved and made available to new generations of researchers. Dinosaur tracks (pp. 28–9) may occasionally be spotted on fallen blocks or on the underside of overhanging slabs of limestone. Insect remains are also well documented from certain beds. The bivalve-rich limestones are still quarried to provide a range of products used in local buildings and further afield.

Exceptional preservation of *Neomiodon*, the dominant bivalve of most of the Purbeck Limestone Group limestones quarried for use as a building material.

The fossilised remains of a small, probably juvenile, ichthyosaur discovered in the Purbeck Limestone Group in Durlston Bay in the early nineteenth century. This is a most unusual find, and came from a series of beds that contain fossils which indicate at least near-normal marine salinity, if not normal marine conditions.

Cottages and Castles

Unfortunately for geologists the UK is a country that is largely covered in a thick layer of vegetation, and consequently it is often only in quarries and road or rail cuttings that the underlying rocks can be seen. Happily, in the Isle of Purbeck, their lives are much easier. While the landscape is intensely rich and the wildlife habitats many and varied, there are great opportunities for access to the geology on the magnificent coastal exposures of the Jurassic Coast and, with permission, in the many small quarries on the limestone plateau. And what is more, dotted around the countryside and villages are other places where the local stone is on display – the buildings.

Stone has been quarried for building purposes since the Romans came to the area nearly 2,000 years ago and, unlike in most other places, the variable nature of the stone meant that different beds were particularly suited to a specific purpose. The cottage walls, roofs, floors and lintels, and the pavements outside are all made from rocks with slightly different characteristics. The Purbeck Limestone Group contains many beds of limestones, all slightly different in composition and all with slightly different characteristics in terms of how they 'split' or how they weathered. These limestones have been given a wonderful variety of names, such as Downs Vein, Thornback and Wetson. The quarrymen knew which particular limestone was best for a particular job to the extent that stone was often, and to some extent still is, taken out of the ground 'to order'. Downs Vein was particularly suited for paving (and flooring), while New Vein had qualities which made it ideal for roof tiles.

Worth Matravers. The variations in the Purbeck limestones mean that different beds are used for walls, roofs and pavements.

London's first proper pavement, complete with kerbstones, was laid down in Duke Street in 1765, and it was made from Purbeck Stone. Many other streets followed, including Fleet Street.

Purbeck stone walling has been a characteristic of these landscapes for hundreds of years. A recent upsurge in interest has seen drystone walling courses for a new generation of wallers, whose work is frequently seen, both restoring walls which have decayed and creating new ones with their own individual styles.

Local stone is also used in the dry stone walls which are such a feature of the limestone plateau above and to the west of Swanage. Drystone walls were normally built with what first came to hand when the boundaries were being drawn. In Purbeck, much of the material came from quarry spoil heaps and stone was carted or sledged to wherever it was needed. Until very recently, many of the walls had fallen into disrepair and livestock were kept in their fields by the addition of barbed wire or electric fences. Happily, though, recent years have seen recognition of the importance of cultural landscapes and a lot of rebuilding work has been undertaken. The Purbeck Keystone Project has offered drystone

Corfe Castle dominates the village of Corfe. The Purbeck Marblers still hold their annual meeting, with its ancient rites and rituals, among houses built from the stone their forebears hewed from the ground. The castle incorporates a significant volume of this locally produced stone.

walling apprenticeships and grants, and funded the restoration and development of the Burngate Stone Centre with support from the Heritage Lottery Fund.

The building of Corfe Castle began soon after the arrival of William the Conqueror in Britain in 1066. The site was selected in a strategic gap in the Chalk ridge, but chalk is a poor building stone and the builders looked to the Purbeck limestones in the ridge to the south. Much of the castle is built from the Broken Shell Limestone, a massive shell-fragment limestone which is very hard and resistant to weathering. This bed can be seen outcropping close to Peveril Point near Swanage, where it forms the ledges that stretch out eastwards and create the turbulent waters of the Peveril race.

At Peveril Point the celebrated Purbeck Marble is exposed in reefs on the shore. This is a sedimentary marble, a limestone which takes a polish, and is made special by the abundance of small shells which belonged to snails thought to have lived in fresh to brackish water (p. 30). The marble has been widely used in cathedrals and minsters, a beautiful example being the shafts around the piers in Salisbury Cathedral. The sharp folds, complicated by faulting, seen at Peveril Point are related to those at Lulworth and Stair Hole, the same complex structure which resulted from the Alpine Orogeny.

Beyond Peveril Point, river-laid Wealden sediments have been eroded to form the great sweep of Swanage Bay. Exposure is poor until the northern cliffs are reached.

Tight folds in the highest Purbeck strata exposed at Peveril Point, Swanage. The disturbance within these strata has been linked to larger-scale folding and associated faults.

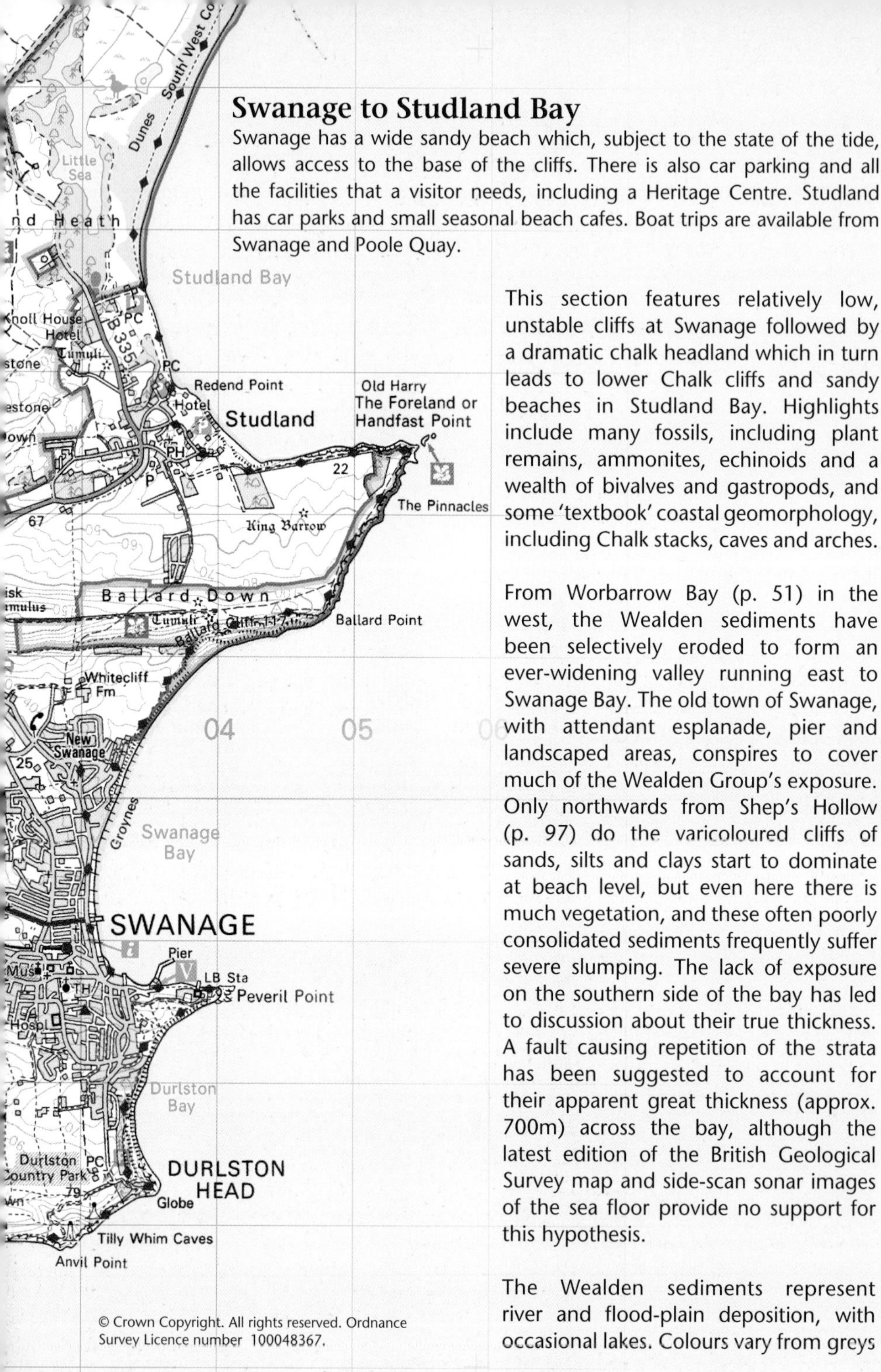

Swanage to Studland Bay

Swanage has a wide sandy beach which, subject to the state of the tide, allows access to the base of the cliffs. There is also car parking and all the facilities that a visitor needs, including a Heritage Centre. Studland has car parks and small seasonal beach cafes. Boat trips are available from Swanage and Poole Quay.

This section features relatively low, unstable cliffs at Swanage followed by a dramatic chalk headland which in turn leads to lower Chalk cliffs and sandy beaches in Studland Bay. Highlights include many fossils, including plant remains, ammonites, echinoids and a wealth of bivalves and gastropods, and some 'textbook' coastal geomorphology, including Chalk stacks, caves and arches.

From Worbarrow Bay (p. 51) in the west, the Wealden sediments have been selectively eroded to form an ever-widening valley running east to Swanage Bay. The old town of Swanage, with attendant esplanade, pier and landscaped areas, conspires to cover much of the Wealden Group's exposure. Only northwards from Shep's Hollow (p. 97) do the varicoloured cliffs of sands, silts and clays start to dominate at beach level, but even here there is much vegetation, and these often poorly consolidated sediments frequently suffer severe slumping. The lack of exposure on the southern side of the bay has led to discussion about their true thickness. A fault causing repetition of the strata has been suggested to account for their apparent great thickness (approx. 700m) across the bay, although the latest edition of the British Geological Survey map and side-scan sonar images of the sea floor provide no support for this hypothesis.

The Wealden sediments represent river and flood-plain deposition, with occasional lakes. Colours vary from greys to purples, reds and greens. Sedimentary structures are especially well displayed when silts and sands have been deposited. Fossils are not abundant, but for the lucky, occasional water-worn dinosaur bones are found washed out on the shore, and blocks of sandstone with the casts of dinosaur tracks are not unknown. The obituary (1962) of one Dr Frank Raw, an academic from the University of Birmingham, paints an entertaining picture of him commandeering a wheelbarrow early one morning to collect such a block found while leading a student field trip. The specimen resides in that university's collection. Dinosaur tracks are a variety of trace fossil (p. 55); the traces of invertebrate animals are also occasionally present in these sediments. Plant material is often abundant. Squashed branches or trunks appear shiny black, breaking into small cubes as the material dries out. Iron pyrites usually laces these specimens and its inherent instability is the humidity-related trigger for the spectacular decay of such material. Less common, but occasionally present, are small fragments of charcoal, a reminder that lightning triggered wildfires across the neighbouring uplands during the often hot, dry summers.

The vegetated and slumped cliffs, along with storm-beach shingle accumulations, in the vicinity of Punfield Cove (see below), have proved challenging to generations of geologists attempting to record and interpret the Lower Greensand Group in the section between the Wealden Group and the Gault Formation. Over the last 150 years the cliffs have sometimes been rather better exposed, and scouring of the beach during severe storms has provided brief glimpses of the foreshore.

View from Durlston Bay, bottom left to Poole Harbour at the top right. Note how the relative hardness of the different geological strata is controlling the development of the coast.

Unfortunately, the ensuing constructive phase has seen these speedily covered and decades have sometimes passed before a similar opportunity arises. The end of the twentieth century did see a couple of events which allowed more thorough investigation and the relationship of these sediments with those on the Isle of Wight to the east and those further west is now much better understood. There is a well-known marine fauna from here, including ammonites, a wealth of bivalves and gastropods, and occasional lobsters. These show that the estuarine and swamp conditions present further west (p. 32), and which at one time reached the Isle of Wight, were banished – at least for a while.

Just east from Punfield Cove, the ridgeway in the shape of Ballard Down intersects the coastline and Chalk dominates. Sadly, the slipping of these strata does much to obscure the transition through Gault and Upper Greensand formations. The undercliff and shore do provide perilous 'exposures' and opportunities to view parts of this succession, though the towering, scarred and unstable Ballard Cliffs above, with great fallen blocks below, are hardly inviting. For those who do venture this far, the blue-black and blue-green to green sediments of the Gault and Upper Greensand are exposed from time to time. The hard calcareous sandstone doggers, known as 'cowstones' from the former, are abundant. Unlike the doggers at Osmington (pp. 20 and 47), any sedimentary structures have been destroyed and complex bioturbation is all that now remains. Ammonite-like spirals of the calcareous worm *Rotularia* often abound. Some of the blocks of Upper Greensand are rich in bivalves, among which small oysters and scallops are especially common.

In the northern corner of Swanage Bay the strata become progressively more steeply inclined to the north (indicated by arrows). The landslides and thick vegetation, along with a storm beach on the foreshore, obscure what would be a fascinating sequence of strata.

Zig Zag Chalk
Formation (part),
Grey Chalk Subgroup
Unconformity
Upper Greensand
Formation (part)

A detached block of sandy Upper Greensand Formation on the shore below Ballard Down. Numerous small oysters known as *Exogyra* are visible – a few examples have been arrowed.

The Chalk Group, initially grey and sometimes glauconitic, becomes a purer limestone and generally white as higher levels are reached. Wavy layers and nodules point to interrupted deposition: fossils are usually fragmentary.

Only visible from a boat, beyond Ballard Point the Chalk is exposed along a south–west to north–east trending cliff stretching out to The Foreland or Handfast Point. Stacks and Old Harry are relicts of the retreating cliff. Once again the forces of the Alpine Orogeny to which some of Dorset's rocks have been exposed are clear to see. The east–west Ballard Down Fault curves through the cliff face – with almost- vertical Chalk to the south and Chalk of the same part of the succession but almost horizontal to the north. The correct interpretation depends to a very great extent on information provided by the seismic surveys and boreholes of the companies searching for oil and gas. Previously geologists had provided four scenarios for the visible structures.

The Ballard Down Fault. The thin black lines have been added to show the dip of the strata on the south side of the fault plane, which curves from top left towards bottom right.

Looking south-west from Handfast Point. Stacks are seen in the foreground and middle distance. Note the natural arch, a precursor of an additional stack being created.

Brief explanations are given for each:

- A north-dipping extensional fault.
  The strata have been stretched and those above the fault slid down and to the north relative to those on the south side of the fault.

- A south-dipping reverse fault pre-dating the formation of the Purbeck Monocline. The fault was rotated as the Purbeck Monocline developed. The strata have been compressed and the reverse fault (strata are forced up over adjacent strata; the fault plane is steeper than 45 degrees) developed. The strata on the south side and above the fault were forced over the strata to the north and below the fault. The formation of the Purbeck Monocline rotated the strata and fault to produce the orientations now seen.

- A north-dipping reverse fault, which developed as the Purbeck Monocline formed. The folding of the strata led to compression, during which the reverse fault developed.

- A north-dipping reverse fault, which must have formed after the development of the Purbeck Monocline.
  The strata have been compressed and folded to form the Purbeck Monocline. A later compressive event led to the development of the north-dipping reverse fault.

The seismic data has given the insight required to conclude that the fourth explanation fits both the observed and the hidden structures.

What is certain is that where our tour comes to an end, on the southern margin of Studland Bay, the most recent interpretation of the junction of the Chalk with the overlying Cenozoic sediments is very different from those made in the past. Where once an erosion surface at the top of the Chalk had been identified, the British Geological Survey has mapped a fault, and while the lowest of the Cenozoic strata

The World Heritage Site terminates at the end of the Chalk outcrop on the southern edge of South Beach, Studland Bay.

preserved elsewhere were always known to have been absent, those sediments once identified as the Paleocene Reading and Eocene London Clay formations have contentiously been reidentified as the Creekmoor Clay Member of the Eocene Poole Formation. Without doubt, further chapters on this part of the story are to be written.

Fossil Fuel

Sir Humphry Davy, the celebrated nineteenth-century chemist, perhaps best remembered for inventing the miner's Davy Lamp, once described geology as a 'science of contemplation'. He is probably right. The excitement of finding outcrops and identifying fossils is one thing, but to try and put it all in context and visualise and understand the environments that ancient animals lived in requires quiet thought. What better place than a country pub for a period of contemplation?

The Isle of Purbeck's pubs and inns have quenched the thirst of quarrymen over two and a half centuries (legend has it that pieces of stone were used as currency back in the eighteenth century), and they have their part to play in the geological story. Most have features or objects of geological interest and a keen observer will find fossils everywhere – in the bar tops, the walls, the paving stones, the stone benches – almost every piece of stone is worth a closer inspection. You are unlikely to find the perfect remains of whole animals, but littered throughout the Purbeck strata are tiny fish teeth and scales, including those of sharks, bits of turtle shell, countless gastropods, billions of bivalves and even coprolites, the fossilised droppings of the denizens of 'Purbeck Park'.

The Bankes Arms in Corfe Castle has a big surprise in the dining room. Here, the tables are made out of local stone (Purbeck Thornback) and inlaid into the table tops are strangely beautiful septarian nodules from the Oxford Clay near Weymouth. They were formed about 160 Ma by chemical reactions in the sediments below the sea floor. As they became more deeply buried under sediment they started to de-water, developing shrinkage cracks. Over the ages, colourful minerals have formed in the cracks, resulting in the remarkable structures that can be seen today.

Table tops made with local Purbeck limestone with cut and polished inlaid septarian nodules.

The Square and Compass at Worth Matravers is perhaps the definitive geological watering hole. The garden is full of trace fossils, including dinosaur tracks, and 'fossilised' ripple marks and mudcracks. There are also large ammonites and pieces of silicified wood.

The Square and Compass at Worth Matravers is surrounded by local stones and houses a museum with local fossils and archaeological finds.

It even has its own museum, which is full of wonderful specimens from the Kimmeridge Clay Formation, Purbeck Limestone and the Chalk groups. The pub has been in the ownership of the Newman family for four generations and they have been, and are still, ardent collectors. In the summer months the Square and Compass also hosts an annual Stone Festival and occasional 'Fossil Roadshows'.

In Studland, it could be argued that they have gone one better. The Bankes Arms Hotel (yes, there are two in Purbeck) has its own brewery and their range of real ales includes 'Fossil Fuel'. Their ales are also sold in the Castle Inn in West Lulworth, where a dinosaur track graces the fireplace in the bar!

Elsewhere in the area there are many other pubs built from the local stone: the Weld Arms in East Lulworth; the New Inn at Church Knowle; the Fox, the Castle and the Greyhound in Corfe; the Kings Arms and Ship in Langton Matravers; and the Royal Oak, Globe, Anchor, Purbeck, White Swan, Black Swan and White Horse in Swanage. Golfers can find dinosaur tracks and large Portland ammonites (*Titanites*) in the clubhouse of the Isle of Purbeck Golf Club. The Village Inn at Ulwell Cottage Caravan Park has a range of Purbeck stone on display behind the fireplace and other fossils set in the wall of the restaurant.

A fine example of a cast of a tridactyl dinosaur track, set in the wall of the Village Inn at Ulwell.

A typical example of a large *Titanites* ammonite. These are frequently seen in parts of the Portland Stone Formation. A 50p piece is included for scale.

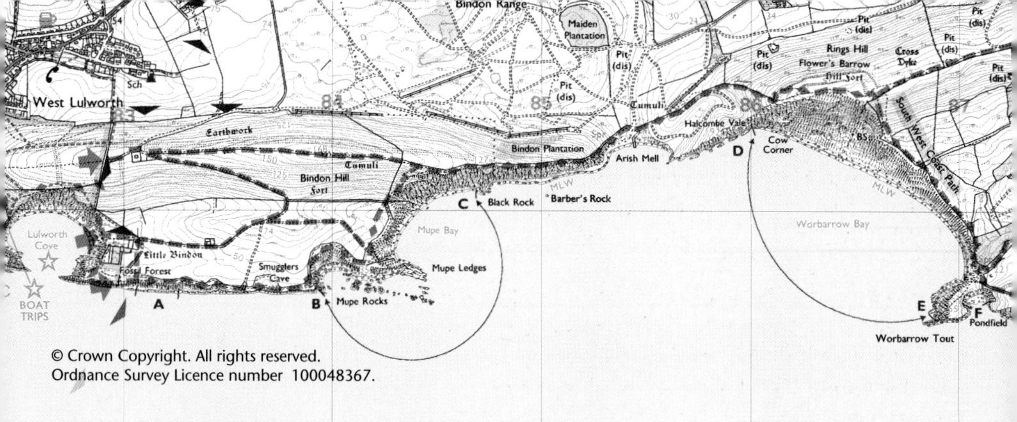

Boat Trip: Lulworth Cove to Worbarrow Tout

A boat trip covering the section from Lulworth Cove to Worbarrow Tout can be undertaken from the cove. Detailed information of sailing times is available at the Lulworth Visitor Centre.

Lulworth Cove is a wonderful place to start a boat trip. The cove itself, with its precipitous back wall of Chalk, provides a relatively calm point to embark on a trip that takes us back through 80 million years of time. The sides of the cove expose strata of the Purbeck Limestone and Wealden groups, with a sliver of the Lower Greensand Group, and then the Gault and Upper Greensand formations. These beds are generally thinner than the equivalent strata exposed further east.

Steeply dipping Purbeck strata at the entrance to Lulworth Cove.

The dramatically striped Purbeck Limestone Group lies above the Portland Group, which almost cuts off the cove from the English Channel. The boat turns due east, running beneath the buttresses of Portland Stone capped with limestones which formed on the floor of an extensive shallow-water lagoon fringed by trees that were able to withstand the arid Purbeck environment. Periodically, movement along a fault caused the forests to be swamped, killing the trees. Microscopic organisms (cyanobacterial colonies called stromatolites) enveloped the dead trees. Holes can be seen in the cliff where tree branches once were.

Looking east from Bacon Hole across Worbarrow Bay to Worbarrow Tout and Gad Cliff.

Bacon Hole viewed from the east. Compare this image with that of Stair Hole (pp. 40–41), where the strata have been tilted to a higher angle and undergone gravity collapse down dip.

Beyond the Fossil Forest the boat offers glimpses into Bacon Hole, where the rock formation (which looks a bit like streaky bacon) is very similar to but less disrupted than that at Stair Hole (pp. 40–41), with the Purbeck strata lying on top of the thicker and tough Portland Stone. At the back of the 'hole', the softer Wealden sediments can be seen spilling over Purbeck strata. A bit further along in Mupe Bay there is evidence of a 'fossil' oil seep in the Wealden strata.

Worbarrow Bay soon comes into view after Mupe Rocks have been passed. The western end of the bay is backed by high Chalk cliffs which occasionally gleam brilliant white after fresh landslides. Halfway along the bay is Arish Mell Gap, through which Lulworth Castle (NGR SY 855822) can be seen. More Chalk and we see the wonderfully colourful cliffs of the Wealden Group. Here, yellows, oranges, reds and browns contrast vividly with the white of the Chalk. Fossils are rare in the Wealden in Purbeck, though a tridactyl dinosaur track has recently been recovered (p. 55). At the far end of Worbarrow Bay the distinctive wedge shape of Worbarrow Tout comes into view, where the Purbeck/Portland sequence seen in Bacon Hole and Lulworth Cove reappears yet again, evidence of a consistent thread which marks this stretch of coast. Beneath the shallow water, a ridge of Portland Limestone connects Mupe rocks with the Tout.

East of Worbarrow Tout the Portland Stone rises high above the sea in the awe-inspiring Gad Cliff. Beyond Kimmeridge Bay in the far distance, St Aldhelm's Head (p. 77) can be seen. As the boat returns to Lulworth Cove, there is an opportunity to look to the west, where on a clear day White Nothe (p. 50) is clearly visible, with Ringstead Bay and Furzy Cliff beyond (pp. 42–43).

Durdle Door

Stair Hole

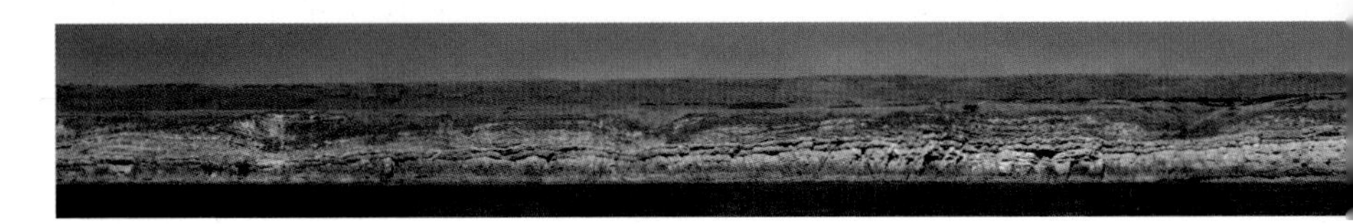

Mupe Bay

Arish Mell

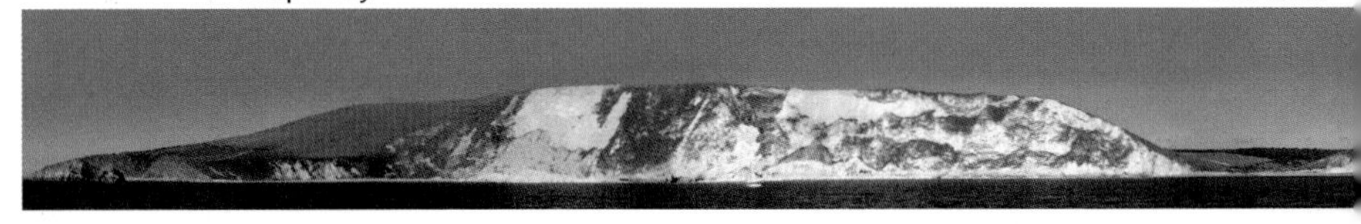

Pondfield Cove

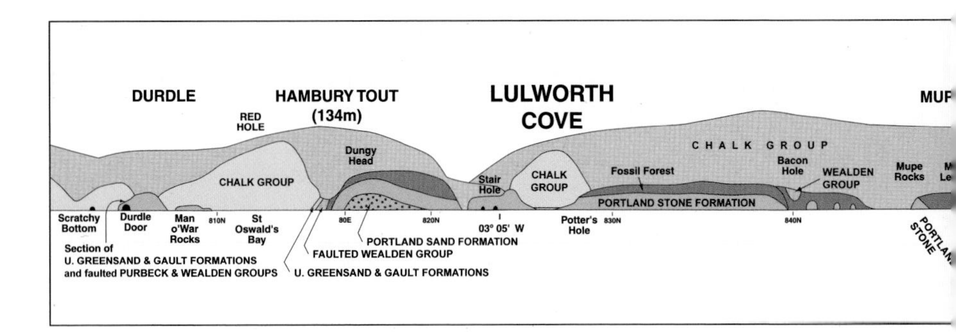

Lulworth Cove

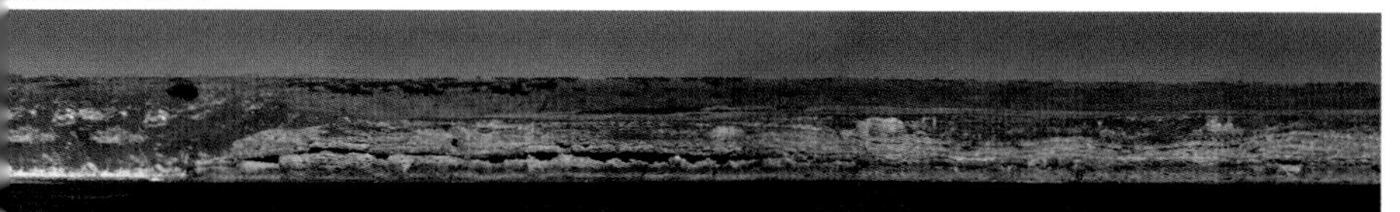

Bacon Hole Mupe Bay

Flower's Barrow Worbarrow Tout

Gad Cliff

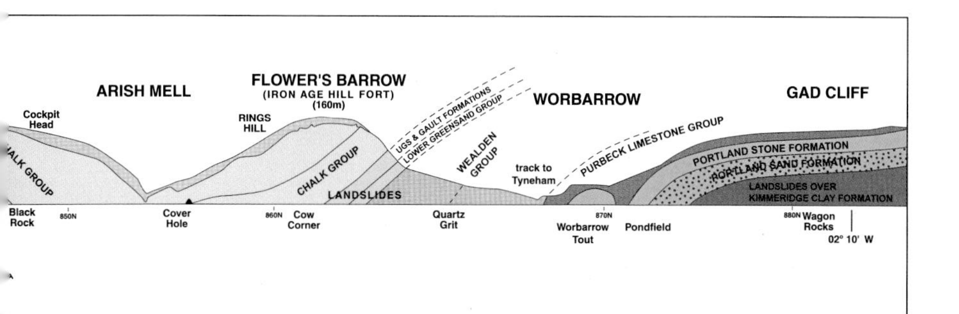

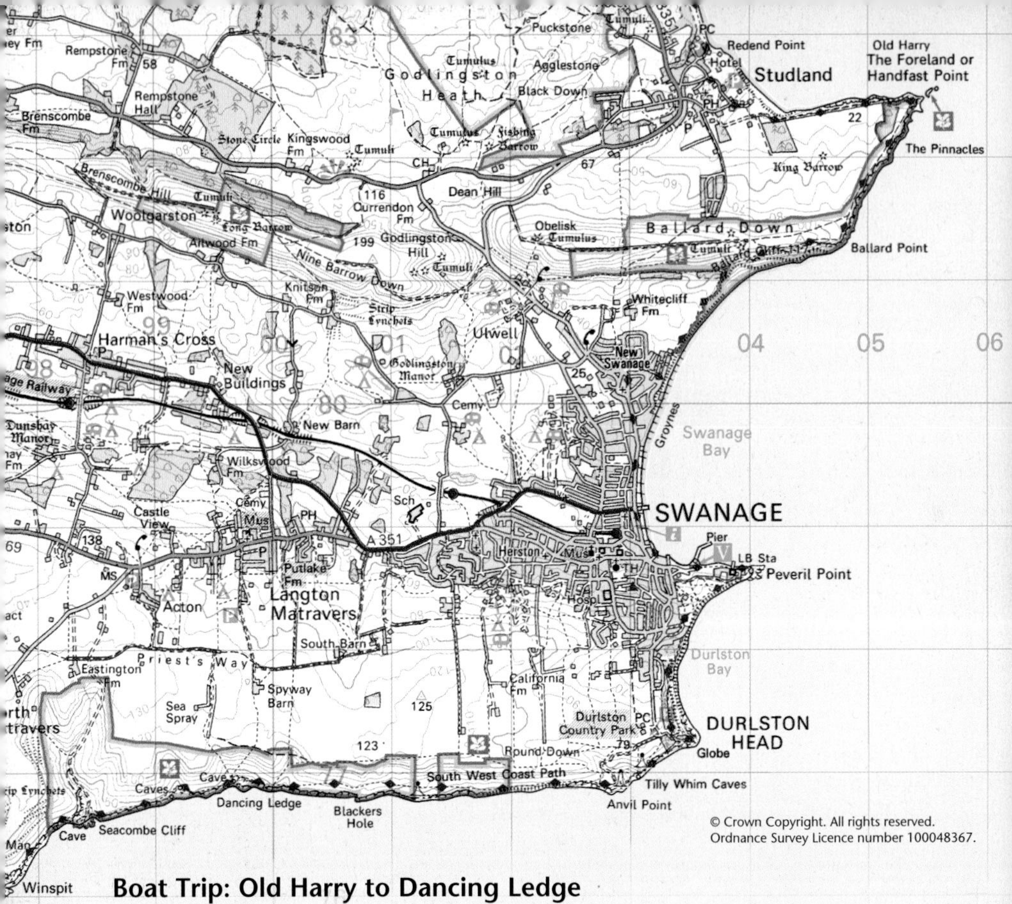

Boat Trip: Old Harry to Dancing Ledge

The boat trip covering the section from Old Harry Rocks to Dancing Ledge can be undertaken from Swanage or Poole Quay. Details of sailings are available from the Swanage or Poole Tourist Information Centres, at the Stone Quay, Swanage, or on Poole Quay.

Old Harry Rocks are classic textbook Chalk stacks, formed by the sea gradually enlarging and eroding out the naturally occurring joints which occur in the Chalk bedrock (p. 111). Look to the east on a clear day and the white cliffs of the Isle of Wight are visible – The Needles being the nearest point. When the last glaciation was at its peak, the two were connected by an extension of the existing Chalk ridge. As the ice slowly melted over the next 25,000 years, sea levels rose (over 140m), the line of Chalk was gradually eroded away, and the western link from the Solent to the English Channel was formed.

The dramatic Chalk cliffs of Ballard Down are structurally very interesting. From Old Harry Rocks southwards the strata runs horizontally until quite suddenly, near Ballard Head, it bends upwards to become almost vertical. The boundary can be seen clearly about 200m to the north of Ballard Head in the form of a curved fault, with a small cave at the base before it drops below sea level. The fault was created by compressive forces after the formation of the Purbeck Monocline (pp. 100 & 102).

The Pinnacle with Ballard Down cliffs to the right and Swanage in the distance.

Round the corner, in Swanage Bay, the Chalk continues to dip steeply and natural weathering between the layers of Chalk has resulted in the octopus-shaped landslide near the north-west corner of the bay.

As the boat leaves Swanage Bay and heads westwards, it crosses Peveril Ledge and here the cliffs change abruptly. Peveril Point marks the transition from the relatively soft Wealden Group sediments of Swanage Bay to the variable Purbeck Limestone Group of Durlston Bay. Here, clays and shales alternate with hard bands of limestone (some of which are quarried as the famous Purbeck building stones). The soft beds weather out, causing large blocks of the harder limestones to fall on to the beach. The result is a beach which is a jumble of stone blocks and smooth pebbles, often beset by a substantial swell, and with a double high water it is a dangerous place to explore.

Durlston Castle (p. 82–3), a Victorian folly now being restored as a World Heritage visitor centre, is dramatically situated on Durlston Head, at the southern end of Durlston Bay. On the north side of Durlston Head, below the castle, a large fault is quite visible from the sea, with the rocks to the north thrown down about 32m. As a result the Portland Stone Formation, which forms the cliffs from here to St Aldhelm's Head (p. 77), is not visible in Durlston Bay – it lies beneath the Purbeck Limestone Group and the sea.

Tilly Whim Caves (p. 85) are not true caves but an old cliff quarry. Last worked in 1810, they became a visitor attraction in the latter part of the nineteenth century and were a key element of George Burt's vision for his Durlston Park development.

Dancing Ledge viewed from the sea.

The 'caves' are now too dangerous to receive human visitors, but have been colonised by wildlife, notably bats.

Dancing Ledge, about 3km west of Durlston Head, is another old cliff quarry. Minor folding and faulting mean that the principal building stones here are lower and therefore easier to access from the sea: tracks, grooved by or for the quarrymen's carts or sledges, can still be seen on the ledge today. The old quarry workings are a popular picnicking spot and a training ground for novice climbers. An odd feature is the small tidal swimming pool on the lower ledge.

During the breeding season the Durlston cliffs are packed with guillemots and razorbills.

Dancing Ledge

Mile Posts

Anvil Point

Durlston Head

Durlston Bay

Swanage

Punfield Cove

Ballard Down

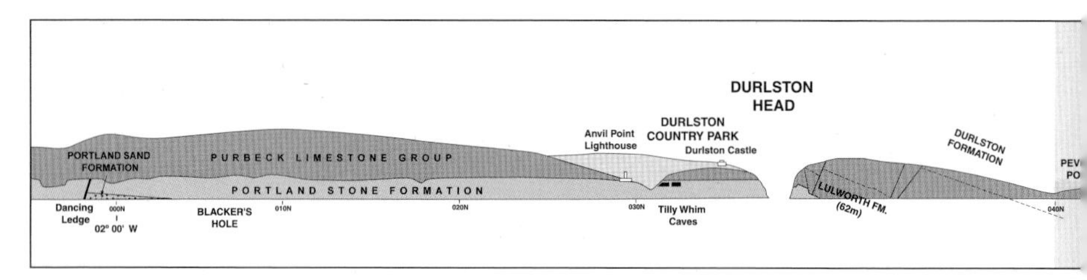

Blackers Hole

Tilly Whim Caves

Durlston Head

Durlston Bay

Swanage

Ballard Down

Handfast Point

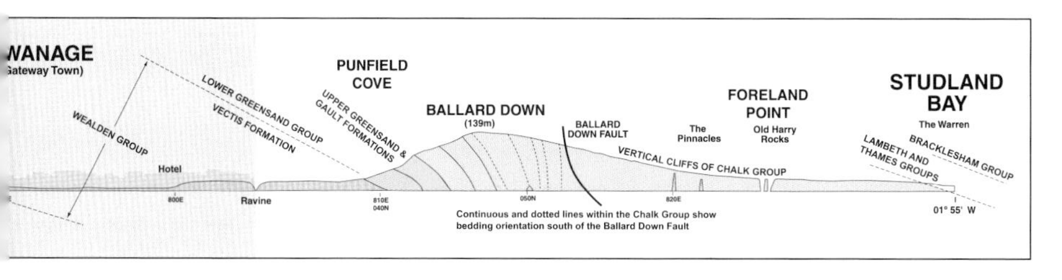

Rocks, Reefs and Races

This geological guide has focused on the exposed geology seen in the cliffs at the eastern end of the Jurassic Coast. To the north lie the familiar hills and valleys of the Isle of Purbeck – a landscape defined by the characteristics of the underlying rocks. To the south lies the wide expanse and largely featureless surface of the English Channel, but a closer look reveals that even here the geological influence is profound. The ebb tide brings to life treacherous tidal races and overfalls which for years have sent ships to an untimely end. Navigational charts highlight the dangers posed by features such as Peveril and Kimmeridge ledges and the Old Harry, St Aldhelm's and Portland races. The turbulence is caused by fast-flowing water running across pronounced geological features on the seabed. These features also form distinct habitats which are home to an extraordinary diversity of marine life. So rich is this area that it is now a candidate Special Area for Conservation (SAC) under the European Habitats Directive.

New technology has dramatically changed our knowledge of this underwater world and the remarkable image shown here was produced using data from DORIS (Dorset Integrated Seabed survey), a collaborative project led by the Dorset Wildlife Trust. The image clearly shows geological features such as faults, folds and hard-rock ledges extending out from the land to the seabed. Superimposed on these ancient structures

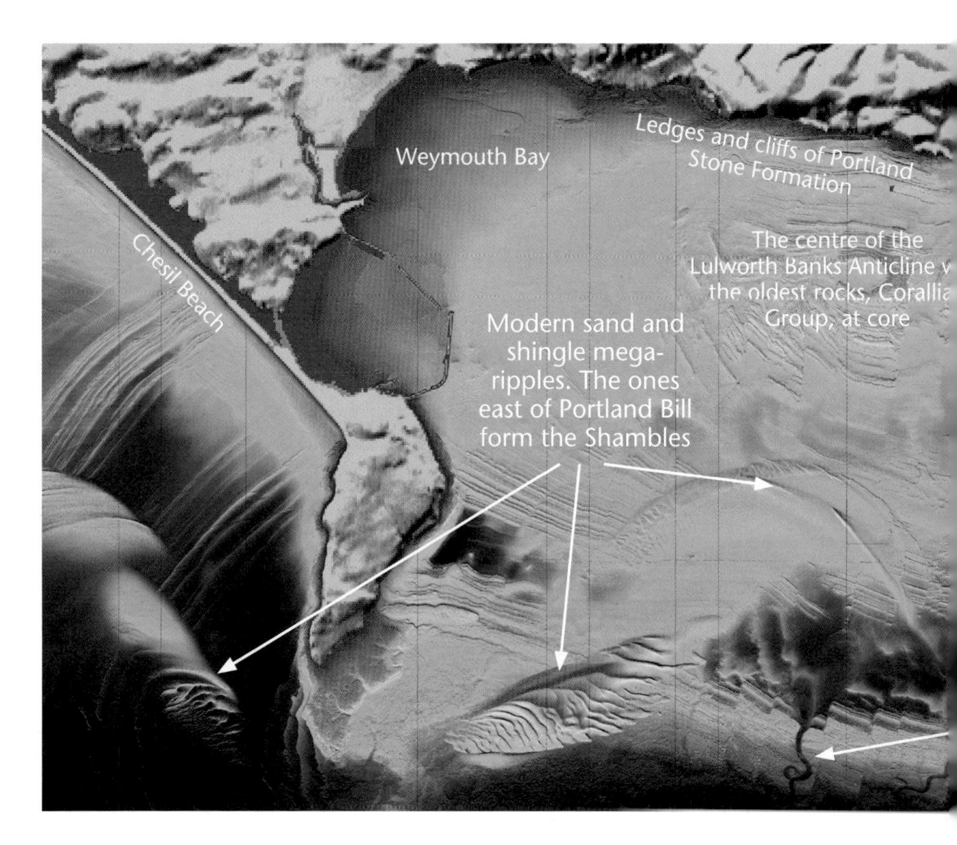

A reef formed from the Broken Shell Limestone is the cause of the Peveril race.

A conger eel awaits its prey under the protection of a rocky ledge.

are present-day sedimentary features such as sand and shingle banks. The image even shows what appear to be the channels of ancient rivers which flowed within our area before the English Channel was created by rising sea levels at the end of the last glacial period.

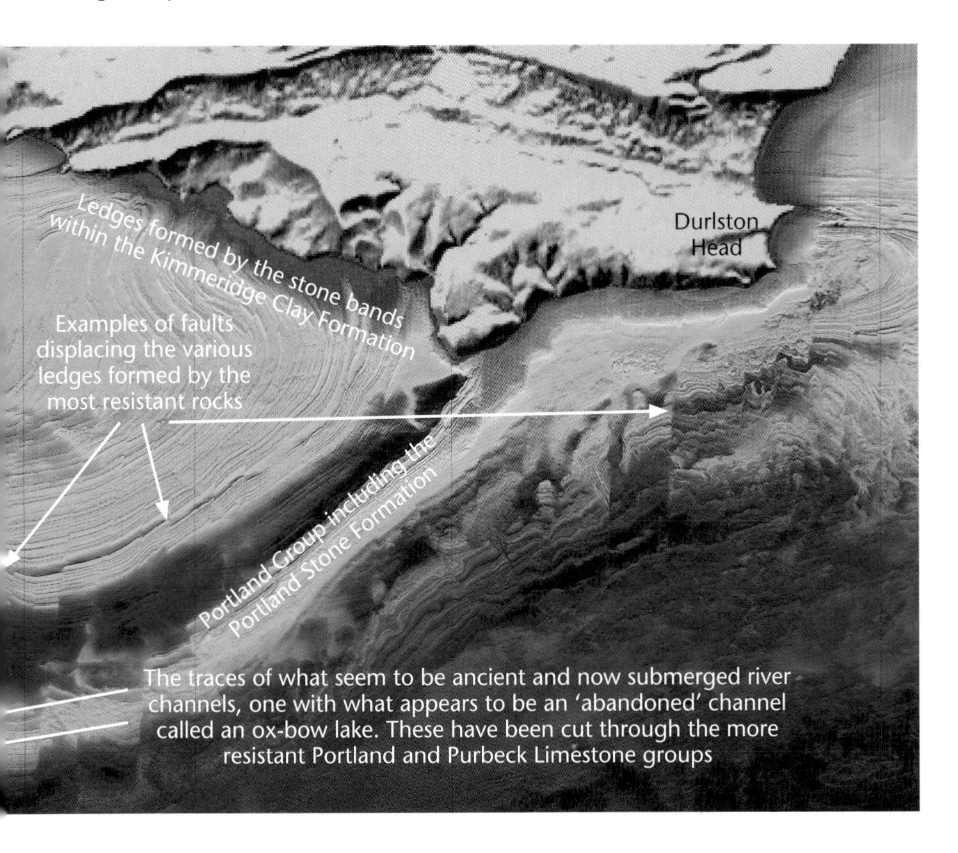

GLOSSARY

The abbreviation Ma stands for millions of years ago. Words in *italics*, except for Latin phrases, are also in the glossary.

alluvium Gravel, sand, silt and clay, deposited by rivers.

Alpine Orogeny The most recent of many episodes of mountain building which have affected the British Isles and which continues to this day.

ammonites Extinct marine invertebrates with a chambered shell which is normally planospirally coiled.

angular unconformity See *unconformity.*

anticlines Strata which have been folded into an arch shape. They range in size from a few metres to tens of kilometres.

assemblages Of fossils may be a life assemblage showing what organisms capable of preservation lived in the same communities; or death assemblages, where the remains of organisms which lived in different environments are brought together after death.

basin An area which undergoes subsidence and will therefore accumulate greater thicknesses of sediment.

bed A distinctive layer of sediment. One or more beds may form a *member.*

bioturbated The disturbance of *sediments* and original *sedimentary structures* by living organisms. The structures created are *trace fossils.*

block An area, often bounded by faults, which is buoyed up compared to surrounding areas. The movement of buried deposits of salt may sometimes be responsible.

brachiopods Marine invertebrates protected by two valves. The resemblance of brachiopods to Roman oil lamps led to them being called lamp shells.

bryozoans Small colonial animals which form skeletons of calcium carbonate (*calcite*), which may encrust solid surfaces or grow in branching tree-like forms.

calciostrontianite A calcium-rich variety of the mineral strontianite (strontium carbonate) which has replaced the *evaporite* mineral *celestine.*

calcite A crystalline form of calcium carbonate which is an important rock-forming mineral. Limestones are predominantly made of calcite, as are the hard parts of many invertebrates.

celestine A mineral composed of strontium sulphate.

Cenozoic (65 Ma to present day) A geological era which encompasses the *Paleogene* and *Neogene* periods.

chert A fine-grained rock composed of the mineral *quartz*. Cherts are hard and dense, ranging in colour from black to brown or yellow. Flint is a purer variety of chert found in the Chalk.

coccoliths Microscopic rings of calcite plates, several of which form the spherical skeleton of a planktonic algae.

concretions Usually spherical masses of cemented sediment which formed during or after the deposition of the host sediment. They are sometimes known as nodules or doggers. See also *septarian nodules.*

corals Sea-anemone-like organisms which have a hard internal skeleton of calcium carbonate (see *calcite*). They may be solitary or form colonies.

correlation The linking together of rocks in different places through, e.g., the distinctive fossils they contain. *Ammonites* are much used in Jurassic and Cretaceous marine sequences.

Cretaceous (145–65 Ma) A period of geological time during which environments across Dorset ranged from fully marine to terrestrial. Sediments include grits, sands and silts, *mudrocks* and *limestones.* The climate was sub-tropical to tropical.

diagenesis The physical and chemical processes to which sediments are exposed after deposition that change their character: e.g. compacting, cementing, the formation of *concretions.*

dip The measurable (in degrees from the horizontal) vertical component of layers of rock, seen as the direction in which they are tilted. Dip is measured at right angles to *strike.*

dogger See *concretions.*

doline A hole created by the dissolution of a *limestone*, either from the surface downwards or by collapse of the surface into a cave.

dolomite A *limestone* composed mainly or entirely of the mineral dolomite (calcium magnesium carbonate) rather than *calcite* (calcium carbonate). Limestones composed of calcium carbonate are sometimes altered to a dolomite, a process called dolomitisation.

echinoids Also known as sea-urchins, a member of the group of animals called echinoderms.

Eocene See *Paleogene.*

evaporites The more soluble minerals or rocks formed when water containing dissolved salts is evaporated.

faecal pellet The droppings of invertebrate animals such as worms, gastropods and crustaceans. They consist of the undigested residue of sediment and food. They are a very small, but form an important component of many *limestones.*

fault A fracture through bedrock and/ or superficial deposits which allows vertical or horizontal movement to take place. Movement may be measured in kilometres. Down-throw is on the side of the fault which has been displaced downwards.

faulting See *fault.*

flint See *chert.*

foraminifera The collective name for what are normally marine, single-celled animals. They generally secrete a calcareous shell, known as a test, which may have one or more chambers.

foresyncline The trough-shaped form of strata on one side of the step-like axis of a *monocline.*

formation A term used by geologists to describe a unit of rock, usually composed of two or more members: e.g. Lulworth

Formation. See also *member* and *group*.

geomorphology The study of the physical features of the Earth's surface and the processes which form them.

glauconite A mineral of complex composition often occurring as sand-sized grains which vary from light green to almost black. Their presence in rocks is usually an indication of deposition in the sea.

group A group is made up of two or more *formations* which, because of their shared characteristics, form a group: e.g. the Lulworth and Durlston formations form the Purbeck Limestone Group.

hardground A *lithified* surface on the sea floor which may suffer erosion and colonisation by organisms before fresh sediment is deposited.

Holocene (*c.*10,000 years ago to the present day) The period of geological time during which man became resident in Dorset, occupying a landscape that continued, and continues even now, to be modified by the movement, erosion and deposition of sediment.

hypersaline Water with a salinity considerably greater than that of ordinary sea water.

joint A fracture in a layer of rock which may run in any direction. Joints form as *sediments* are *lithified* and are subjected to tensional stress, folding and *faulting*.

Jurassic (199–145 Ma) A period of geological time during which predominantly marine sands, silts, *mudrocks* and *limestones* were deposited across Dorset. Large marine reptiles swam in the seas and, later, dinosaurs walked across parts of the county. The climate was tropical to sub-tropical.

limestone A rock composed of calcium (see *calcite*) or calcium magnesium carbonate (see *dolomite*).

lithified Literally turned to stone. This happens when mineral cements bind the sediment particles, solidifying what was once unconsolidated, even soupy, sediment.

longitudinal coast A geomorphological term which describes a coast that is parallel to the dominant trend (*strike*) of the rocks.

member Layers of sediment (*beds*) that are sufficiently distinctive to be recognised and mapped across a geographical area. A *formation* usually comprises two or more members. See also *bed, formation* and *group*.

Mesozoic (251–65 Ma) A geological era, encompassing the *Triassic, Jurassic* and *Cretaceous* periods.

microfossils Collective term for a wide variety of plant and animal fossils of very small size, requiring optical or electronic microscopy for their identification and study. They include the *foraminifera, ostracods, radiolaria,* conodonts, pollen and spores. They often play an important part in the dating and correlation of strata.

molluscs A group of invertebrate animals which include gastropods, bivalves and ammonites.

monocline See *Purbeck Monocline*

mudrocks Sediments composed of fine particles with a size less than 0.06mm.

Neogene (23 Ma–present) A period of geological time which incorporates the Miocene (23–5.33 Ma), Pliocene (5.33–2.65 Ma), *Pleistocene* and *Holocene.* Only sediments of the latter two have been recognised in Dorset.

nodules See *concretions.*

ostracods Very small members of the phylum Arthropoda. They are protected by bivalved shells and occupy a wide variety of aquatic environments.

palaeo-fault A *fault* which is known to have been active one or more times during the Earth's history. They are most readily identified when buried beneath later deposits, these providing evidence of the latest time at which movement occurred: i.e. a *terminus ante quem.*

Paleocene See *Paleogene.*

Paleogene (65–23 Ma) A period of geological time which incorporates the Paleocene (65–56 Ma), Eocene (56–34 Ma) and Oligocene (34–23 Ma). The first two of these are represented by strata in Dorset. The climate was sub-tropical.

penecontemporaneous Almost coincident with.

phosphatised The condition where the casts of fossils and sediment surfaces are enriched in phosphate minerals, becoming a darker brown or black colour.

Pleistocene (2.65 Ma–present) The period of time in which the Earth has experienced the most recent in a long history of glaciations dating back to the Pre-Cambrian.

pseudomorph The crystal of a mineral which has been altered and is preserved either as another variety of mineral or a rock.

Purbeck Monocline Folded strata where the rocks on each side of the steep and sometimes overturned middle limb (axis) are more or less gently dipping, forming a *syncline* to the north and an *anticline* to the south. The surface exposure of the Monocline's axis follows the line of the Chalk ridgeway from near Bat's Head in the west to Ballard Down in the east.

quarr An underground working for stone on the Isle of Purbeck.

quartz A variety of silica and an abundant mineral. The major constituent of most sands. *Flint* and *chert* are related.

radiolarians Single-celled microscopic marine organisms which create intricate skeletons of opal, a variety of silica.

sabkha Mudflats fringing an inland lake or the sea which are subjected to high temperatures with consequent evaporation. *Evaporites* form below and over the surface of the mud. The name is from the Middle East,.where they are relatively common.

sedimentary structures Evidence of processes which were affecting *sediments* as they were deposited and before they were *lithified.*

sediments Particles of rock or mineral grains ranging from very small (muds), through silts and sands to larger pebbles, cobbles, etc.

seismic survey A method of investigating the hidden geology below the surface using shock waves generated by either an explosion or special vehicles which vibrate the ground.

septarian nodules Localised enrichment of clays with calcium carbonate leads to the formation of spheres or flattened spheres of hardened sediment. Loss of water causes a network of concentric and radial fractures to form, which may fill with calcite, giving rise to a chambered or septate appearance.

serpulids Marine worms living in often complex calcium carbonate (see *calcite*) tubes which they secrete.

side-scan sonar A survey technique used to produce a detailed picture of the sea floor using sound waves transmitted from a pod towed behind a ship, which in turn receives the sound waves reflected from the sea floor.

solifluction The process by which sediment moves down-slope under gravity, in response to the alternate freezing and thawing of water.

sponges Largely marine animals with soft bodies, normally given shape and strengthened by siliceous or calacareous skeletons.

strata Another word for *beds*: (singular) stratum.

strike The directional trend of strata. Strike is measured at right angles to the *dip.*

stromatolite Primitive plants (cyanobacteria) which by non-photosynthetic processes form banded calcium carbonate. They are important sediment producers.

syncline Strata which have been folded into a trough shape. They range from a few metres to tens of kilometres

tectonic plates The slabs of rock which cover and move across the Earth's surface.

trace fossils Evidence left in *sediments* by the many activities of animals: e.g. movement, feeding and protection.

transgression When sea level rises and more land is covered by the sea, with the result that fringing seas become deeper.

transverse coast A geomorphological term which describes a coast that is cut at or nearly at right angles to the dominant trend (*strike*) of the rocks.

Triassic (251–199 Ma) A period of geological time during which terrestrial gravels, sands, silts and clays were deposited across Dorset. Salt deposits formed.

tridactyl Three-toed.

tuberculate Bearing tubercles.

unconformity The contact between rocks where sedimentation has not been continuous. A considerable gap in time may be represented. The unconformity may be obvious, with folded and eroded rocks overlain by flat-bedded *sediments,* giving an angular unconformity, or bedding may be similar above and below, giving a non-angular unconformity (a disconformity).

ACKNOWLEDGEMENTS

The authors wish to thank the Jurassic Coast Trust for inviting them to write the second of the coastal guides for the World Heritage Site. Professor Denys Brunsden (Series Editor) has provided guidance and constructive criticism. Professor Vincent May kindly read the entire text and provided many helpful comments and revised and redrew previously published figures of landslips.

We are very grateful to the following for providing advice on various aspects of the book, including the provision and use of illustrations: Alan Holiday and Jo Thomas (DIGS Group), Dr Tim Palmer (Palaeontological Association), Professor Zofia Kielan-Jaworowska (Instytut Paleobiologii PAN), Richard Edmonds (Jurassic Coast Team), Trev Haysom, Charlie Newman, Adrian Brokenshire, and Steve Etches for access to his collection and allowing us and Julian Sawyer to take photographs. Dr Doug Cole generously provided images of the burning cliff.

We wish to acknowledge with gratitude the following, who have provided us with images held by their institutions: Jon Murden, Jenny Cripps and George Wickham (Dorset County Museum); Alison Hawkins (Hastings Museum and Art Gallery); Eliza Howlett and Wendy Shepherd (Oxford University Museum of Natural History); Neil Ellis (Joint Nature Conservation Committee); Daragh Kenny (National Gallery Picture Library, London); Peter Tinsley (Dorset Wildlife Trust); Peter Sills, Susan Sutterby, Andrea Marshall, Jonathan Lewis (Coastal Publishing); Katie Black (Durlston Country Park).

The DORIS image was produced using data from the Dorset Integrated Seabed survey, a collaborative project involving the Dorset Wildlife Trust, the Maritime and Coastguard Agency, the Channel Coastal Observatory and the Royal Navy, with major funding from Viridor Credits Environmental Company. Other partners include Natural England, the Dorset Strategic Partnership, the University of Southampton and the National Oceanography Centre.

Finally, we are indebted to our respective families, Jan Turnbull, and Tom and Jamie Ensom, for their interest and support while this guide was being written.

PICTURE CREDITS

Source and copyright details of the illustrations in this book are as follows (page number is followed by position, where t = top, m = middle, b = bottom, l = left, r = right)

Mervyn Arkell: 9; British Geological Survey: 10 bl&br, 12, 61m; Coastal Publishing: Front cover, 15, 16-17, 22, 25t, 43b, 49t, 52t, 56-57, 58, 65b, 73b, 80t&b, 82-83, 85b, 97b, 100b, 101; Dr Doug Cole: 24t; DIGS Group & Anthea Dunkley :53b; DIGS Group & Carol Roberts: 26-27, 27b, 28-29; Dorset County Museum: 23br,

76tl, 89tr, 90tc, 90tr, 90-91b; Dorset Wildlife Trust: 116-117b; Durlston Country Park: 86tr, 86mr;Richard Edmonds: 11t, 54br, 61t, 88b, 108 – 109 (x5), 114– 115 (x6);Paul Ensom: 20tr&b, 29t&b, 30br, 31b, 33b, 34bl, 35b, 37t, 44br, 46bl, 47b, 49b, 55tl,ml,bl, 56tl,ml, 62l (x4), 62b, 63 inset, 67t, 69t, 70b, 71t, 72br, 74t,bl,mr,br 75mr, 81br, 84t, 86bl,br, 87m, 88t, 92tr, 98b, 99; Monique Feist; 30bl; Jane Francis; 55tr;Hastings Museum and Art Gallery: 91tl; JNCC: 48t&b, 61b, 78, 79t (A-C); Jurassic Coast Team: 3tl, 40-41, 45b, 64b, 66, 105br; Jurassic Coast Trust: 6b, 8b, 13b; Jonathan Lewis: 106; Professor Vincent May: 48t,b, 78, 79t (A-C); National Gallery Picture Library: 44t;Ordnance Survey; 42-3t, 50-51t, 68-9b, 77t, 96l, 105t, 110b, 124mr; Oxford University Museum of Natural History: 92b; Palaeontological Association: 90tr; Francesca Radcliffe; 51b; Julian Sawyer: 3bl, 38br, 39t, 75bl,br; Dennis Smale; 89b; David Sole 127br; Peter Szekely: 117tl,tr; Swanage Museum; 82 inset; Richard Tayler: 19tr; Malcolm Turnbull: 36-37b, 62A&C, 65tr, 71br, 76tr, 79b, 81t, 83 insets, 87t, 93b, 94tr, 94b, 95b, 100tl,ml, 102b, 103mr,br, 104mr,b, 107t, 111, 112b, 113b; © 2000: Dorset County Council, M.R. House, NERC (Permit Number: IPR/68-13c) and The Jurassic Coast Trust; 108b – 109b & 114b – 115b;Graham Warboys: 60, 62D, 63; The Weld Estate; 67b (1-4).

MAPS

Ordnance Survey:

1:50,000 Sheets 194 (Dorchester & Weymouth) and
195 (Bournemouth & Purbeck)

1:25,000 Explorer™ OL 15, Purbeck & South Dorset

Geological Survey: (1:50,000 Sheets)
West Fleet and Weymouth. Sheet 341 and part of 342

Swanage. Sheet 342 (east) and part of 343

FURTHER READING

General accounts and guides:

Arkell, W.J., 1933, *The Jurassic System in Great Britain*, OUP, 253 pages.

Arkell, W.J., 1947, *Geology of the Country around Weymouth, Swanage, Corfe and Lulworth. Memoir of the Geological Survey of Great Britain: England and Wales*, HMSO, 386 pages.

Brunsden, D. (Editor), 2003, *The Official Guide to the Jurassic Coast, Dorset and East Devon's World Heritage Coast: A Walk through Time*, Coastal Publishing, 64 pages.

Brunsden, D., and Goudie, A., 1997, *Classic Landforms of the East Dorset Coast*, Classic Landform Guides, Geographical Association, Sheffield, 48 pages.

Davies, G.M., 1956, *The Dorset Coast*, A&C Black, 128 pages.

Dorset County Council, Devon County Council and Dorset Coast Forum, 2000, *Nomination of the Dorset and East Devon Coast for Inclusion in the World Heritage List*, Dorset County Council, 150 pages.

Dorset's Important Geological/Geomorphological Sites Group, 2005 '[Walk] 3, Acton – Langton Matravers – Dancing Ledge', in *Beneath Your Feet: 5 Country walks to explore the rocks that form the landscape of Purbeck and Poole Bay Cliffs.*

Ensom, P.C., 1998, *Discovering Dorset – Geology*, Dovecote Press, 89 pages.

House, M.R., 1993, *Geology of the Dorset Coast*, The Geologists' Association, 164 pages.

May, V.J., 2003, Ballard Down, Dorset (SZ 041 825), in May, V.J., and Hansom, J.D., *Coastal Geomorphology of Great Britain*, Geological Conservation Review Series, No. 28, Joint Nature Conservation Committee, Peterborough, pp. 176–81.

May, V.J., 2003, The Dorset Coast: Peveril Point to Furzy Cliff (SY 697 816 – SZ 041 786), in May, V.J., and Hansom, J.D., *Coastal Geomorphology of Great Britain*, Geological Conservation Review Series, No.28, Joint Nature Conservation Committee, Peterborough, pp. 624-42.

Melville, R.V., and Freshney, E.C., 1983, *British Regional Geology: Hampshire Basin and Adjoining areas*, 6th Edition, HMSO, 146 pages.

Strahan, A., 1898, *The Geology of the Isle of Purbeck and Weymouth*, Memoirs of the Geological Survey: England and Wales, HMSO, 278 pages.

The geological history of England and Wales:

Brenchley, P.J., and Rawson, P.F., 2006, *The Geology of England and Wales*, The Geological Society of London, 559 pages.

Bibliography:

Thomas, J. and Ensom, P.C., 1989, *Bibliography and Index of Dorset Geology*, Dorset Natural History & Archaeological Society, 102 pages.

VISITING THE JURASSIC COAST

The Jurassic Coast is well served by its 'Gateway Towns' and villages, which provide a good range of accommodation, museums and visitor centres throughout the year. There are mainline rail links to the area from London and Bristol. Exeter and Bournemouth airports are both about half an hour's journey from the coast.

Exploring the World Heritage Coast is best done on foot or by sea. The entire coast is accessible via the South West Coast Path National Trail, which is easy to follow by looking for the acorn symbol. A network of footpaths link to the coast path and make circular walks possible. Full details of access are given in the book. Guided walks and events take place throughout the year and details can be found in Tourist Information Centres and by logging on to www.jurassiccoast.com. All visitor centres and many museums offer regular walks, talks and other events.

There are numerous boat trip operators offering Jurassic Coast tours along the coast and this is really one of the best ways of seeing the World Heritage Site. Tourist Information Centres have more details, and boat trips are also usually advertised around local harbours and quaysides.

Public transport is available between many of the towns and villages along the coast. Please call Traveline on 0871 200 22 33 for specific public transport information.

SAFETY

On the beach

- Always stay away from the cliffs.
- Do not climb the cliffs. Rockfalls can happen at any time.
- Beware of landslips and mudflows, especially during or after wet weather.
- Always aim to be on the beaches on a falling tide and beware of the incoming tide, especially around headlands. Be sure to check the tide tables.
- Be very careful on rocky foreshores, which often have slippery boulders.
- Beware of large waves in rough weather.
- Some stretches of coast involve strenuous walks along shingle or bouldery foreshore – make sure you are walking within your fitness capabilities.
- Make sure you have the right equipment for the conditions, such as good boots and waterproof clothing.
- Take precautions against the sun if appropriate.

On the coast path

- Keep well away from the cliff edges and ensure that children and dogs are kept under control.
- Observe all restricted access and diversion signs – this is a active and changing coast.
- Follow the Countryside Code, which can be viewed at http://www.naturalengland.org.uk/ourwork/enjoying/countrysidecode.

Emergencies

In an emergency ring 999 and ask for the Coast Guard, but be aware that mobile phone coverage in some areas is very limited.

Collecting fossils

- The best, and safest, place to look for fossils is on the beach, where the sea has washed away soft clay and mud.
- Do not collect from or hammer into the cliffs, fossil features or rocky ledges.
- Keep collecting to a minimum. Avoid removing *in situ* fossils, rocks or minerals.
- The collection of specimens should be restricted to those places where there are plenty of fossils.
- Only collect what you need – leave something for others.
- Add to the potential scientific importance of your collected specimens by keeping a record of where they came from and when they were found.
- Never collect from walls or buildings. Take care not to undermine fences or other structures.
- Be considerate and don't leave a site in an unsightly or dangerous condition.
- Some landowners do not wish people to collect – please observe notices.
- Do not use a hammer on flint or chert, which shatter into sharp fragments.

The Geological Fieldwork Code should be read before carrying out fieldwork. The code may be viewed and downloaded at http://www.geoconservation.com/GCCdocs/fieldworkcode.pdf.

If you make an important find please contact the nearest visitor centre, or the World Heritage Team on 01305 225101

WHERE TO FIND OUT MORE

Coastal Visitor Centres

Durlston Castle	01929 424443
Fine Foundation Marine Centre, Kimmeridge	01929 481044
The Heritage Centre, Lulworth Cove	01929 400587
National Trust Visitor Centre, Studland	01929 450259
National Trust Visitor Centre, Corfe Castle	01929 481294

Tourist Information Centres

Swanage – Shore Road	01929 422885
Wareham – South Street	01929 552740

Museums and Attractions

Corfe Castle Town Museum	No telephone
Dorset County Museum, Dorchester	01305 262735
Langton Matravers Museum	01929 423168
Purbeck Mineral and Mining Museum	No telephone
Swanage Museum and Heritage Centre	01929 421427
Swanage Railway Museum, Corfe Castle	01929 425800
Wareham Town Museum	01929 553448

Traveline

Public Transport information	08712002233

Other useful contacts

Dorset AONB	01305 228239
Dorset DIGS Group	www.dorsetrigs.org.uk
Natural England, Dorchester	01305 257086
South West Coast Path Association	01752 896237

For other information and a list of useful web sites please visit

www.jurassiccoast.com